Assessment Program A

VISIONS

Language ✧ Literature ✧ Content

Mary Lou McCloskey

Lydia Stack

THOMSON
★ ™
HEINLE

Australia ✧ Canada ✧ Mexico ✧ Singapore ✧ United Kingdom ✧ United States

THOMSON

HEINLE ™

VISIONS ASSESSMENT PROGRAM A
Mary Lou McCloskey and Lydia Stack

Publisher: *Phyllis Dobbins*
Director of Development: *Anita Raducanu*
Director, ELL Training and Development: *Evelyn Nelson*
Developmental Editor: *Tania Maundrell-Brown*
Associate Developmental Editor: *Yeny Kim*
Associate Developmental Editor: *Kasia Zagorski*
Editorial Assistant: *Audra Longert*
Production Supervisor: *Mike Burggren*
Marketing Manager: *Jim McDonough*
Manufacturing Manager: *Marcia Locke*
Photography Manager: *Sheri Blaney*
Development: *Proof Positive/Farrowlyne Associates, Inc.*
Design and Production: *Proof Positive/Farrowlyne Associates, Inc.*
Cover Designer: *Studio Montage*
Printer: *Globus Printing Company*

Printed in the United States of America.
6 7 8 9 10   08 07 06 05

For more information, contact Heinle, 25 Thomson Place, Boston, Massachusetts 02210 USA, or you can visit our Internet site at http://www.heinle.com

For permission to use material from this text or product contact us:
Tel   1-800-730-2214
Fax   1-800-730-2215
Web www.thomsonrights.com

ISBN: 0-8384-5297-3

Contents

STUDENT TESTS

STUDENT RESOURCES

TEACHER RESOURCES

Introduction and Overview

The *Visions* Assessment Program was designed to ensure standards-based accountability for teachers and students alike. It begins with a Diagnostic Test to assess what students already know and to target students' needs in specific skill areas. Throughout the book, students take a Chapter Quiz at the end of each chapter. At the end of each unit, they take a Unit Test. The Assessment Program ensures ongoing as well as summative evaluation with the Mid-Book and End-of-Book Exams. Portfolio Assessment is also taken into account to measure the students' overall progress.

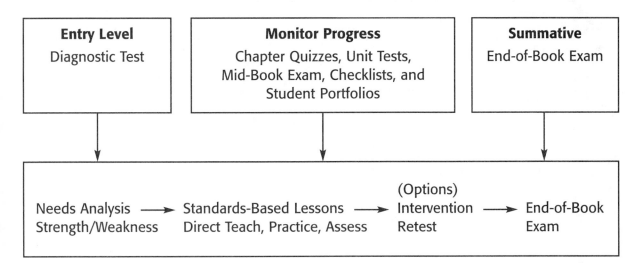

ExamView® is a CD-ROM assessment instrument that allows teachers to create and customize their *Visions* Assessment Program. The Chapter Quizzes, Unit Tests, Mid-Book Exam, and End-of-Book Exam can be customized by adding, deleting, editing, or rearranging questions from the test bank of standards-based assessment items. *ExamView*® also allows teachers to create and/or customize tests for the purpose of retesting after intervention.

ENTRY LEVEL PLACEMENT

Heinle recognizes that English Language Learners usually take a placement test such as the *Language Assessment Scales* (LAS), the *California English Language Development Test* (CELDT), the *IDEA Proficiency Test* (IPT), or the Woodcock Muñoz. Heinle provides correlations to these placement tests so teachers know where to place students in the *Visions* program. Contact your local Heinle/Thomson Learning Sales Representative for more information about these correlations.

ASSESSMENT REFERENCE CHART

The reference chart below provides an overview of the assessment instruments, page numbers, and purpose of the assessment tools in the *Visions* Assessment Program.

	Name	Pages	Purpose of Assessment
Entry Level	**Diagnostic Test**	1–6	To enable teachers to ascertain their students' skills in vocabulary, reading, grammar, spelling, and writing, and to perform a Needs Analysis in order to target specific instructional needs.
Monitor Progress	**Chapter Quizzes**	7–96	To monitor students' ongoing progress in vocabulary, grammar, reading, and writing. There are 27 Chapter Quizzes.
	Unit Tests	17–102	To monitor students' ongoing progress toward meeting strategies and standards in vocabulary, grammar, reading, and writing at the end of each unit. There are 6 Unit Tests.
	Mid-Book Exam	55–60	To monitor students' ongoing progress toward meeting strategies and standards in vocabulary, grammar, reading, and writing as taught throughout the first three units of the book.
	Student Resources Checklists	115–133	To promote student responsibility in meeting the standards. Students self-assess their strengths and weaknesses for purposes of reteaching if necessary.
Summative	**End-of-Book Exam**	103–108	To measure students' achievement and mastery in meeting the standards in vocabulary, reading, and writing as taught throughout the book.
	Peer Editing Checklists	117–120	To collaboratively involve classmates in giving and gaining feedback on their progress toward meeting the standards in writing.
	Active Listening Checklist	124	To collaboratively involve classmates in giving and gaining feedback on their progress in the area of listening and speaking during oral presentations.
Monitor Progress	**Teacher Resources** Listening, Speaking, Reading, Writing, Viewing, and Content Area Checklists	134	To track ongoing progress of students in all domains of the standards, and to serve as a vehicle in planning instruction.
	Reading Fluency	116, 136	To check students' progress in learning to read silently and aloud with expression, and to adjust their reading rates according to the purpose of their reading.
	Rubrics	136–137	To evaluate students' overall performance using a fixed measurement scale and a list of criteria taken from formal and informal outcomes. These rubrics should be part of each student's permanent record.
	Portfolio Assessment	115	To involve students in self-reflection on their progress in meeting their learning goals. This ongoing assessment is a collection of student work that exhibits the student's best efforts and progress.
	***ExamView®* CD-ROM**	CD-ROM	To empower teachers to choose and customize test items to meet students' targeted needs; items chosen may be used to retest after intervention activities.

ENTRY LEVEL

DIAGNOSTIC TEST

The following subtests appear in the Diagnostic Test. These subtests may be taken all at once or at multiple diagnostic sessions.

A. **Vocabulary Meaning Subtest** This subtest assesses the learner's vocabulary and ability to derive meaning from context. The ability to comprehend and read contextually is an indispensable skill, just as successful contextual reading requires an adequate vocabulary.

B. **Word Study Subtest** This subtest assesses the learner's ability to recognize parts of words (such as suffixes, prefixes, and roots) and to sound out words. It also assesses the dictionary skills covered in each level of *Visions* that pertain to word analysis.

C. **Reading Comprehension Subtest** This subtest evaluates the learner's ability to answer questions about a silently-read passage. The learner's reading rate (fluency) may also be measured in addition to his/her understanding of the reading.

D. **Reading Strategies Subtest** This subtest assesses the successful use of various reading strategies presented in *Visions*.

E. **Grammar/Usage Subtest** This subtest evaluates skills that match the standards taken from the Grammar Focus section of *Visions*.

F. **Spelling Subtest** This subtest assesses the learner's spelling skills. It mirrors the spelling skills found in the Writing section of the *Visions* Activity Book.

G. **Writing Subtest** This subtest assesses the learner's writing skills. Skills from this section mirror the writing practice given in *Visions*. Learners are asked to write in sentences.

H. **Writing Conventions Subtest** This subtest assesses the learner's capitalization and punctuation skills. Students must identify mistakes using a multiple-choice format.

MONITORING PROGRESS

CHAPTER QUIZZES

Each chapter has a two-page quiz with 20 multiple-choice questions and one writing prompt. The following subtests within the Chapter Quizzes reflect the skills that have been taught in the various sections of each chapter. A scoring guide has been included to ensure consistency and fairness.

A. **Vocabulary** (based on the Build Vocabulary and Word Study sections of the chapter)

B. **Text Structure/Elements of Literature**

C. **Reading Strategies**

D. **Grammar/Usage**

E. **Writing**

UNIT TESTS

Each unit has a six-page test with 40 multiple-choice questions and one writing prompt. There are nine subtests within the Unit Tests. Each subtest reflects the skills within the unit and the skills found on state tests. A scoring guide has been included to ensure consistency and fairness. The nine subtests are as follows:

A. **Reading** Allows students to apply and assess the skills they have learned in the unit.

B. **Reading Comprehension** Assesses literal, inferential, and higher-order thinking through multiple-choice questions.

C. **Reading Strategies** Assesses skills emphasized in Standards Assessment, such as identifying main idea/details, making inferences, drawing conclusions, and so on.

D. **Elements of Literature** Assesses knowledge of literary elements emphasized in Standards Assessment, such as plot, setting, character, point of view, and so on.

E. **Vocabulary** Assesses vocabulary skills emphasized in Standards Assessment, such as prefixes, suffixes, root words, and so on.

F. **Grammar/Usage** Assesses knowledge and skills emphasized in grammar and usage Standards Assessment.

G. **Editing** Assesses students' ability to identify problems in writing and to correct or improve them.

H. Writing Conventions Assesses knowledge and application of spelling, capitalization, and punctuation.

I. Writing Assesses students' writing skills. The writing prompt is centered on the unit theme. Planning guidelines or tips are included to help students write.

SUMMATIVE EVALUATION

MID-BOOK AND END-OF-BOOK EXAMS

Mid-Book Exam Assesses skills covered in *Visions*, Units 1–3.

End-of-Book Exam Assesses skills covered in *Visions*, Units 1–6.

Both exams reflect the type and nature of testing done on standardized tests. They help prepare students to take language arts and English language-learner types of tests. The nine subtests within each Mid-Book and End-of-Book Exam are the same as the Unit subtests but require more higher-order thinking. Students are required to write a three-paragraph essay in *Visions* A and a five-paragraph essay in *Visions* B & C.

STUDENT RESOURCES

PORTFOLIO ASSESSMENT

Introducing the portfolio

Distribute a folder to each student in the class. Direct students to write their names on their portfolios and make a design, such as a coat-of-arms, that pictorially tells something about them. Write the word *portfolio* on the board and explain that their portfolio is a collection of their best work. At least one piece of their work from each unit should go into their portfolio. Their portfolios should contain the best examples of the effort, progress, and achievements they have made throughout *Visions.*

Student participation in selecting pieces

Students should save all of the work they do in each unit in a "work" folder. At the end of each unit, students will select their best work from this collection to add to their portfolio.

Model the portfolio selection process by distributing the *Portfolio: Activity Rating and Reflection Sheet* (p. 115). Then, write on the board: "What is the piece or activity I liked the most?" Demonstrate removing the selected piece from their work folder and placing it in the portfolio.

Discuss the criteria for selecting pieces

Discuss with the class the reasons for making a portfolio selection. Add their responses to a list on the board. Be sure to explain to students the following characteristics of a portfolio:

> • **It is continuous and ongoing.** A portfolio contains samples of work that stretch over an entire marking period and can be accompanied by art, videotapes, and computer graphics.
> • **It provides for student reflection** about students' own work and learning.
> • **It contains a variety of different assessment tools** including student checklists.

Paulson, F.L., Paulson, P.R., and Meyer, CA. (1991, February). "What Makes a Portfolio a Portfolio?" *Educational Leadership,* pp. 60–63.

Portfolio: Activity Rating and Reflection Sheet

Show students how to fill out the *Portfolio: Activity Rating and Reflection Sheet.* Have students work with a partner to share their work and discuss their responses before completing the sheet. When students have completed the sheet, have them attach it to the piece that they select to place in their portfolio.

Completing the portfolio process

Explain where students should put their portfolios for storage until the next time they use them. Also explain where students should keep their "work" folders. The pieces of work gathered from the unit that were not selected to include in the portfolio may be taken home.

READING FLUENCY

Practice

Throughout *Visions*, students receive practice in all the basic subskills of reading fluency.

Each lesson is designed to cover and scaffold fluency instruction for English language learners. The subskills include word recognition, chunking, phrases, oral reading, silent reading, reading comprehension, adjusting rate for purpose, repeated reading, and reading with expression.

The Reading Fluency Chart (p. 116) serves two assessment purposes. It serves as a record for:

1. The number of words per minute a student reads aloud.
2. The number of words per minute a student reads silently.

After students have recorded their progress on their Reading Fluency Charts, the students' grade level in reading fluency can be determined by referring to the rubric below.

Average rates for reading for students in Grades 2–12

Grade Equivalent	Standard Words per Minute
2.5	121
3.5	135
4.5	149
5.5	163
6.5	177
7.5	191
8.5	205
9.5	219
10.5	233
11.5	247
12.5	261

Source: Carver (1990)
National Center for Education Statistics

CHECKLISTS

Student Checklists are an integral part of the portfolio evaluation process. They provide feedback and a record of student progress in listening, speaking, reading, writing, and viewing. These checklists are referenced in the *Visions* Teacher Editions and are reproducible from the Assessment Program. The checklists and evaluation forms provided are:

Student Checklist	Page
Portfolio: Activity Rating and Reflection Sheet	115
Reading Fluency Chart	116
Responding to Peers' Writing: *EQS*	117
Peer Editing Checklist	118
Editor's Checklist	119–120
Narrative Checklist	121
Persuasive Checklist	122
Oral Presentation Evaluation Sheet	123
Active Listening Checklist	124
Speaking Checklist	125
Viewing Checklist	126
Word Study and Spelling	127
Word Study and Spelling Assessment Chart	128
Independent Reading Record	129
Student Self-Assessment	130
Activity and Project Reflection	131
Test-Taking Tips	132–133

TEACHER RESOURCES

CHECKLISTS

The Teacher Resource reproducible checklists should be used to plan and evaluate instruction. The *Lesson Plan Checklist for The Sheltered Instruction Observation Protocol* (*SIOP*) (pp. 134–135) can be used during the Across Content Areas sections of *Visions*. The *Rubric for Oral Reading Fluency* (p. 136) will help you assess the progress of your students during the Build Reading Fluency sections of the student book. You may want to give students a copy of the *Rubric for Oral Presentations* (p. 137) that you will use for grading. The following important checklists serve as a guideline for standards-based accountability. Four marking periods are provided for each standard.

- Listening and Speaking Standards Assessment Checklist, pp. 138–139
- Reading Standards Assessment Checklist, pp. 140–141
- Writing Standards Assessment Checklist, pp. 142–143
- Viewing and Representing Standards Assessment Checklist, p. 144

Name _____ Date _____

Answer Sheet

For Diagnostic Test, Unit Tests, Mid-Book Exam, and End-of-Book Exam

Fill in the circles of the correct answers. Erase mistakes well.

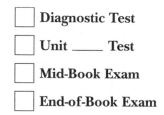

☐ **Diagnostic Test**

☐ **Unit ____ Test**

☐ **Mid-Book Exam**

☐ **End-of-Book Exam**

1. ⓐ ⓑ ⓒ ⓓ   11. ⓐ ⓑ ⓒ ⓓ   21. ⓐ ⓑ ⓒ ⓓ   31. ⓐ ⓑ ⓒ ⓓ

2. ⓐ ⓑ ⓒ ⓓ   12. ⓐ ⓑ ⓒ ⓓ   22. ⓐ ⓑ ⓒ ⓓ   32. ⓐ ⓑ ⓒ ⓓ

3. ⓐ ⓑ ⓒ ⓓ   13. ⓐ ⓑ ⓒ ⓓ   23. ⓐ ⓑ ⓒ ⓓ   33. ⓐ ⓑ ⓒ ⓓ

4. ⓐ ⓑ ⓒ ⓓ   14. ⓐ ⓑ ⓒ ⓓ   24. ⓐ ⓑ ⓒ ⓓ   34. ⓐ ⓑ ⓒ ⓓ

5. ⓐ ⓑ ⓒ ⓓ   15. ⓐ ⓑ ⓒ ⓓ   25. ⓐ ⓑ ⓒ ⓓ   35. ⓐ ⓑ ⓒ ⓓ

6. ⓐ ⓑ ⓒ ⓓ   16. ⓐ ⓑ ⓒ ⓓ   26. ⓐ ⓑ ⓒ ⓓ   36. ⓐ ⓑ ⓒ ⓓ

7. ⓐ ⓑ ⓒ ⓓ   17. ⓐ ⓑ ⓒ ⓓ   27. ⓐ ⓑ ⓒ ⓓ   37. ⓐ ⓑ ⓒ ⓓ

8. ⓐ ⓑ ⓒ ⓓ   18. ⓐ ⓑ ⓒ ⓓ   28. ⓐ ⓑ ⓒ ⓓ   38. ⓐ ⓑ ⓒ ⓓ

9. ⓐ ⓑ ⓒ ⓓ   19. ⓐ ⓑ ⓒ ⓓ   29. ⓐ ⓑ ⓒ ⓓ   39. ⓐ ⓑ ⓒ ⓓ

10. ⓐ ⓑ ⓒ ⓓ   20. ⓐ ⓑ ⓒ ⓓ   30. ⓐ ⓑ ⓒ ⓓ   40. ⓐ ⓑ ⓒ ⓓ

Name _____ Date _____

Answer Sheet

For Chapter Quizzes

Fill in the circles of the correct answers. Erase mistakes well.

Chapter _____ Quiz

1. ⓐ ⓑ ⓒ ⓓ   11. ⓐ ⓑ ⓒ ⓓ

2. ⓐ ⓑ ⓒ ⓓ   12. ⓐ ⓑ ⓒ ⓓ

3. ⓐ ⓑ ⓒ ⓓ   13. ⓐ ⓑ ⓒ ⓓ

4. ⓐ ⓑ ⓒ ⓓ   14. ⓐ ⓑ ⓒ ⓓ

5. ⓐ ⓑ ⓒ ⓓ   15. ⓐ ⓑ ⓒ ⓓ

6. ⓐ ⓑ ⓒ ⓓ   16. ⓐ ⓑ ⓒ ⓓ

7. ⓐ ⓑ ⓒ ⓓ   17. ⓐ ⓑ ⓒ ⓓ

8. ⓐ ⓑ ⓒ ⓓ   18. ⓐ ⓑ ⓒ ⓓ

9. ⓐ ⓑ ⓒ ⓓ   19. ⓐ ⓑ ⓒ ⓓ

10. ⓐ ⓑ ⓒ ⓓ   20. ⓐ ⓑ ⓒ ⓓ

Diagnostic Test Results Chart

Record students' scores for each section of the diagnostic test here.

Student Name	A. Vocabulary Meaning	B. Word Study	C. Reading Comprehension	D. Reading Strategies	E. Grammar/ Usage	F. Spelling	G. Writing	H. Writing Conventions
1.								
2.								
3.								
4.								
5.								
6.								
7.								
8.								
9.								
10.								
11.								
12.								
13.								
14.								
15.								
16.								
17.								

Intervention/Reteaching Component Guide

This chart serves as a guide to the *Visions* components you can use to reteach the skills tested on the Unit Tests, the Mid-Book Exam, and the End-of-Book Exam.

	Student Book	Teacher Edition	Activity Book	Student Handbook	Student CD-ROM	More Grammar Practice workbook	Teacher Resource Book
A. Reading Comprehension	X	X			X		
B. Reading Strategies	X	X		X	X		X
C. Elements of Literature	X	X	X	X	X		
D. Vocabulary	X		X	X	X		X
E. Grammar/ Usage	X		X	X	X	X	
F. Editing				X			
G. Writing Conventions		X	X	X	X		
H. Writing	X		X	X			X

Student Name _____

Individual Progress Chart for Intervention

Chapter Quizzes

The purpose of this chart is to record the student's progress and to use it as a basis for intervention and reteaching. Note sub-sections of the quizzes where the student is weak and target those areas as part of the intervention plan.

Formal Assessment

Record the student's scores for each sub-section of the quizzes.
Write the number correct over the number of possible points for each sub-section.

	Unit 1					Unit 2					Unit 3					Unit 4				Unit 5				Unit 6			
	1	2	3	4	5	1	2	3	4	5	1	2	3	4	5	1	2	3	4	1	2	3	4	1	2	3	4
A. Vocabulary	/32	/32	/28	/32	/24	/24	/24	/24	/24	/24	/24	/28	/24	/28	/28	/20	/24	/24	/20	/28	/24	/20	/20	/28	/24	/28	/20
B. Text Structure/ Elements of Literature	/16	/12	/16	/16	/24	/32	/32	/32	/32	/32	/24	/24	/16	/28	/16	/24	/20	/28	/24	/20	/16	/28	/20	/16	/28	/20	/32
C. Reading Strategies	/12	/12	/12	/12	/16	/12	/12	/12	/12	/12	/12	/16	/20	/12	/16	/12	/20	/16	/16	/12	/16	/20	/16	/16	/16	/16	/12
D. Grammar/ Usage	/20	/24	/24	/20	/16	/12	/12	/12	/12	/12	/20	/12	/20	/12	/20	/24	/16	/12	/20	/20	/24	/12	/24	/20	/12	/16	/16
E. Writing	/20	/20	/20	/20	/20	/20	/20	/20	/20	/20	/20	/20	/20	/20	/20	/20	/20	/20	/20	/20	/20	/20	/20	/20	/20	/20	/20

Student Name _____

Individual Progress Chart for Intervention
Unit Tests, Mid-Book Exam, End-of-Book Exam

The purpose of this chart is to record the student's progress and to use it as a basis for intervention and reteaching. Note sub-sections of the tests where the student is weak and target those areas as part of the intervention plan.

Formal Assessment

Write the number correct over the number of possible points for each sub-section.

	Unit 1 Test	Unit 2 Test	Unit 3 Test	Mid-Book Exam	Unit 4 Test	Unit 5 Test	Unit 6 Test	End-of-Book Exam
Reading Comprehension	/20	/20	/20	/20	/20	/20	/20	/20
Reading Strategies	/10	/10	/10	/10	/10	/10	/10	/10
Elements of Literature	/10	/10	/10	/10	/10	/10	/10	/10
Vocabulary	/10	/10	/10	/10	/10	/10	/10	/10
Grammar/Usage	/10	/10	/10	/10	/10	/10	/10	/10
Editing	/10	/10	/10	/10	/10	/10	/10	/10
Writing Conventions	/10	/10	/10	/10	/10	/10	/10	/10
Writing	/20	/20	/20	/20	/20	/20	/20	/20

Authentic Assessment

Record your observations of the student's strengths and needs.

Student Portfolio	Teacher Observation (language development, content, organization, creativity, other)
Unit 1	
Unit 2	
Unit 3	
Unit 4	
Unit 5	
Unit 6	

Interpersonal Skills	Teacher Observation (participation, cooperation, other)
Unit 1	
Unit 2	
Unit 3	
Unit 4	
Unit 5	
Unit 6	

Rubric for Writing Assessment

1. Use this rubric as a guide for writing instruction.
2. Also use it to score the Writing on Chapter Quizzes, Unit Tests, the Mid-Book Exam, and the End-of-Book Exam.
3. Do not expect students to demonstrate all criteria for each trait.
4. Add the number of points to obtain the writing score. 4 points x 5 traits = 20 points total possible score
5. Record the score on the Progress Charts on pages xiv and xv.

TRAITS	4 points	3 points	2 points	1 point
1. Development of Ideas Are ideas presented and supported insightfully?	• Ideas are thoroughly developed. • Development reflects thought. • Ideas are presented insightfully. • Compositional risks enhance writing.	• Ideas are reasonably well-developed. • Development shows thought. • Ideas show thought. • Few compositional risks evident.	• Idea development is attempted. • Omitted information creates minor gaps between ideas.	• Little or no idea development evident. • Ideas are a summary of a known writing, movie, or TV show. • Omitted information creates significant gaps between ideas.
2. Organization Are ideas ordered logically from sentence to paragraph?	• Thought progression is smooth and controlled. • Transitions are meaningful. • Order of ideas is logical. • Organizational strategies enhance presentation of ideas.	• Thought progression is generally smooth and controlled. • Transitions are mostly meaningful. • Ideas are mostly linked. • Effective organizational strategies. • Minor wordiness and/or repetition.	• Thought progression is somewhat smooth and logical. • More transitions are needed. • Ideas are somewhat linked. • Ineffective organizational strategy. • Some wordiness and/or repetition.	• Progression of thought is not logical. • Inappropriate use or lack of transitions. • There is no organizational strategy. • Wordiness and/or repetition inhibits progression of ideas.
3. Voice Does the writer engage reader and show individuality?	• Reader is engaged throughout. • Composition sounds original. • Individuality and unique voice are expressed.	• Reader is generally engaged. • In general, composition sounds original. • Writing generally expresses individuality.	• Reader is engaged sporadically. • Parts of the composition sound original. • Writing expresses some individuality.	• Writing does not engage the reader. • Little or no sense of the writer's voice. • Composition does not sound original. • Writing does not express individuality.
4. Fluency and Focus How well do individual paragraphs and the whole composition flow together?	• Focus is sustained throughout. • Writing has sense of completeness. • Introduction/conclusion are meaningful. • All/most of writing contributes to development and quality.	• Writing is generally focused. • Clear relationship between ideas. • Few sudden shifts in ideas. • Overall sense of completeness. • Introduction/conclusion add depth. • Most of writing contributes to development and quality.	• Writing is somewhat focused. • Writer shifts ideas, but ideas are related. • Some sense of completeness. • Introduction/conclusion are superficial. • Some of writing is extraneous.	• Writing is not focused. • Writer shifts ideas abruptly. • Little or no sense of completeness. • Introduction/conclusion are inadequate. • Much of writing is extraneous. • Topic is weakly connected to prompt.
5. Conventions Are spelling, capitalization, punctuation, grammar, usage, sentence structure appropriate?	• Writing shows a strong/consistent command of conventions. • Minor errors occur during compositional risks. • Words, phrases, and sentence structure enhance effectiveness.	• Writing shows good command of conventions. • Minor errors do not disrupt fluency. • Words, phrases, and sentence structure are generally appropriate and contribute to effectiveness.	• Writing shows limited control of conventions. • Errors weaken fluency. • Simple or inaccurate words and phrases and awkward sentences limit effectiveness.	• Writing has severe/frequent errors in conventions. • There is an overall lack of fluency. • There is frequent misuse/omission of words and phrases. • There are frequent awkward sentences.
6. *Presentation Does format ease and enhance understanding?	• Penmanship is pleasing. • Margins and spacing enhance understanding. • Devices (headings, bullets, numbers, etc.) clarify and organize information.	• Penmanship is clear. • Margins and spacing are appropriate. • Devices (headings, bullets, numbers, etc.) are somewhat effective.	• Penmanship is difficult to interpret. • Margins and spacing are inconsistent. • Devices (headings, bullets, numbers, etc.) are superficial.	• Penmanship is illegible. • Margins and spacing are confusing. • Inappropriate use or lack of devices (headings, bullets, numbers, etc.).

* Do not include in writing assessment scores.

Name _____ Date _____

Grade

DIAGNOSTIC TEST

A. ➤ Vocabulary Meaning Choose the correct answer. *(10 points)*

Example: A celebration is usually _____.
  a. blue
  (b.) happy
  c. square
  d. sad

1. The father of your mother is your _____.
  a. uncle
  b. grandmother
  c. grandfather
  d. aunt

2. To *enjoy* something means to _____ it.
  a. ride
  b. hate
  c. like
  d. push

3. I get home from school, then I do my homework, and finally I eat dinner. What do I do <u>first</u>?
  a. eat dinner
  b. go to bed
  c. do my homework
  d. get home from school

4. Lara *flung* the shell in the ocean. *Flung* means _____.
  a. threw
  b. ate
  c. found
  d. saw

5. When an event is a *custom*, it is _____.
  a. usual
  b. unusual
  c. difficult
  d. late

B. ➤ Word Study Choose the correct answer. *(10 points)*

6. What two words make up the compound word *birthday*?
  a. bir + thday
  b. birt + hday
  c. birth + day
  d. birthd + ay

7. The word *beautiful* means "full of beauty." The word *graceful* means _____.
  a. full of joy
  b. full of food
  c. full of hope
  d. full of grace

---

cel·e·brate /sɛl ə ˌbreɪt/ *v.* **-brated, -brating, -brates 1** to do something special (like having a party) to mark an occasion: *I celebrated my birthday with friends in a restaurant.* **2** to honor: *Many towns celebrate Independence Day with a parade.* *–n.* celebration /ˌsɛl ə 'breɪʃən/.

---

8. Look at the dictionary entry. How do you break *celebrate* into syllables?
  a. cel·ebrate
  b. cel·e·brate
  c. cele·brate
  d. celeb·rate

9. Look at the dictionary entry. What are *-brated, -brating,* and *-brates*?
  a. definitions
  b. related words
  c. endings for celebrate
  d. beginnings for celebrate

10. The teacher was _____ that the students did well on the test.
  a. please
  b. pleased
  c. pleasing
  d. pleasure

1

DIAGNOSTIC TEST (continued)

C. ➤ **Reading Comprehension:** Choose the correct answer based on the reading selections. *(20 points)*

Come to the Library

1   Come to the library. Please come in. Are you a student? This is a good place to study. Please close the door, softly. Everyone is quiet here. Students study in quiet places.

2   There are many books here. There are many different kinds. You can use them for your classes. There are books about other countries, like Japan and Mexico. You can find history books, too. Take one. Read about the old days. Or read a literature book. Read stories. Stories are one kind of literature.

3   The library is a quiet place. So it is a good place to study. Many students come here. They use the computers. They study their lessons. They find answers to questions in books.

---

11. What place is this reading about?
 a. Mexico
 b. school
 c. the library
 d. the office

12. What can you find here?
 a. telephones
 b. books
 c. doors
 d. food

13. Why is this a good place to study?
 a. It is quiet.
 b. It is a large place.
 c. Many students come here.
 d. Stories are one kind of literature.

14. What are stories?
 a. quiet places
 b. one kind of literature
 c. answers to questions
 d. places to study

15. Who finds answers to questions in books?
 a. computers
 b. libraries
 c. students
 d. books

DIAGNOSTIC TEST *(continued)*

The Great Storytelling Contest

Do you like to exaggerate?

Come tell your best story to a crowd of enthusiastic listeners.

We'll vote on:
a. who has the best story, and
b. whether we think your story is true or made-up!

Who?	Open to all!
When?	August 12
Where?	The Fairgrounds
How much?	General Admission: $7
	Senior Admission (over 54): $3
	Child Admission (4–11): $1
	Children Under 3: Free
	Storytellers: FREE!

16. To win the contest, you must _____.
   a. always vote
   b. always listen
   c. tell the best story
   d. tell a true story

17. Admission to the contest is _____.
   a. free for all children
   b. $54 for seniors
   c. $7 for most people
   d. $3 for storytellers

18. The contest takes place at _____.
   a. the storyteller's place
   b. the fairgrounds
   c. general admission
   d. the fair

19. The contest takes place in _____.
   a. summer
   b. winter
   c. fall
   d. spring

20. To enter The Great Storytelling Contest, you should be _____.
   a. rich
   b. a storyteller
   c. a child under 3
   d. a listener

DIAGNOSTIC TEST *(continued)*

D. ➤ Reading Strategies: Choose the correct answer based on the reading selections. *(10 points)*

21. What is the title of the first reading?
    a. Come to the Library
    b. The Great Storytelling Contest
    c. The library is a good place to study.
    d. Do you like to exaggerate?

22. How many paragraphs are there in *Come to the Library*?
    a. 1
    b. 2
    c. 3
    d. 4

23. What is the main idea of *The Great Storytelling Contest*?
    a. There will be a storytelling contest.
    b. Many people exaggerate.
    c. Stories are told in the evenings.
    d. Storytelling happens in August.

24. Who are always at *The Great Storytelling Contest*?
    a. children under 3
    b. seniors
    c. storytellers
    d. general admission

25. The crowds at *The Great Storytelling Contest* are _____.
    a. exaggerators
    b. listeners
    c. free
    d. storytellers

DIAGNOSTIC TEST (continued)

E. ➤ Grammar/Usage: Choose the correct answer. *(10 points)*

26. My name is Miguel, and I _____ fifteen years old.
    a. be
    b. am being
    c. have
    d. am

27. Yesterday, our class _____ to the Museum of Science.
    a. go
    b. wented
    c. went
    d. gone

28. Rosa _____ to bed at 9 o'clock every night.
    a. go
    b. is going
    c. goes
    d. be going

29. I am going to the movies with Lara and Tony tonight. I will meet _____ there at 7 P.M.
    a. we
    b. they
    c. them
    d. us

30. Jose did not come to school today. He _____ be sick.
    a. can
    b. might
    c. would
    d. is

F. ➤ Spelling: Choose the correct answer. *(10 points)*

31. _____ your answers on a piece of paper.
    a. Writ
    b. Rit
    c. Write
    d. Rite

32. One lady sat by the window. The other two _____ sat by the door.
    a. ladi
    b. lady
    c. ladies
    d. ladie

33. One child hid under the chair. The other two _____ hid in the closet.
    a. child
    b. childs
    c. child's
    d. children

34. I feel sick. I ate _____ much birthday cake.
    a. to
    b. tu
    c. too
    d. tou

35. Rosa and Miguel _____ for their mother.
    a. wated
    b. waded
    c. weted
    d. waited

DIAGNOSTIC TEST *(continued)*

G. ➤ **Writing:** Write a paragraph about the topic below. Write your paragraph on a piece of paper. *(20 points)*

> **Writing Prompt** Write a paragraph to describe yourself. What do you look like? What do you like to do?

Planning Guide
- ❏ On a piece of paper, list words that describe what you look like.
- ❏ List things that you like to do.
- ❏ Organize these ideas into a paragraph.

H. ➤ **Writing Conventions:** There is one mistake in each sentence. Choose the letter that is under the mistake. *(10 points)*

Example: <u>What</u> do <u>you</u> <u>do</u> after <u>school.</u>
       a   b c   ⓓ

36. <u>the</u> <u>rooster</u> crows <u>when</u> the sun <u>rises</u>.
    a   b   c   d

37. <u>In</u> <u>september,</u> students <u>go</u> back <u>to</u> school.
    a   b   c   d

38. <u>What</u> day is <u>today.</u> <u>Oh!</u> I thought it was
    a   b   c
<u>Saturday!</u>
    d

39. <u>The</u> ball <u>red</u> bounced <u>down</u> the <u>stairs.</u>
    a   b   c   d

40. <u>He</u> <u>love</u> to swim <u>and</u> <u>skateboard.</u>
    a   b   c   d

Grade

QUIZ Unit 1 • Chapter 1

A. ➤ Vocabulary: Choose the correct answer. *(32 points: 4 points each)*

Example: Which word can you add to a web about vegetables?
  a. bread
  (b.) beans
  c. rice
  d. apple

1. Which word can you add to a web about animals?
  a. car
  b. lizard
  c. tree
  d. house

2. Which word can you add to a web about weather?
  a. park
  b. rain
  c. television
  d. picnic

3. The words mansion, apartment, and condominium belong on a web about _____.
  a. vacations
  b. food
  c. homes
  d. jobs

4. The words tulip, rose, carnation, and violet belong on a web about _____.
  a. flowers
  b. people
  c. buildings
  d. dancing

5. A word made up of two words is a _____.
  a. synonym
  b. verb
  c. noun
  d. compound word

6. The afternoon sun burned my shoulders. Which word is a compound word?
  a. afternoon
  b. burned
  c. neck
  d. shoulders

7. He tripped on his shoelace and fell down. Which word is a compound word?
  a. tripped
  b. shoelace
  c. fell
  d. stairs

8. What does the word doghouse mean?
  a. a dog that sits on top of a house
  b. a house built by a dog
  c. a house built for a dog to sleep in
  d. a house with dogs painted on it

B. ➤ Text Structure/Elements of Literature: Read and choose the correct answer. *(16 points: 4 points each)*

"A Gathering"

1 Come gather for the celebration.
   Are we all here?

2 It takes two rooms and three tables
   To fit us all in.

3 Uncle commands our attention and
   gives thanks.
   Then we eat.

4 And eat, and eat, and eat, and eat.

---

9. This reading is a _____.
  a. personal narrative
  b. play
  c. poem
  d. informative article

10. What words tell you this reading is in first-person point of view?
  a. we, us, our
  b. come, celebration, two
  c. Uncle, attention, eat
  d. gather, here, thanks

QUIZ Unit 1 • Chapter 1 (continued)

11. In line 3, <u>Uncle commands our attention</u>. What do you think the scene is like before this?
    a. a quiet, calm scene
    b. a house decorated with colored lights
    c. watching football on television
    d. a busy, talkative group of people

12. What is the author writing about?
    a. graduating from high school
    b. dinner with relatives
    c. running in a track meet
    d. reading the menu at a restaurant

C. ➤ Reading Strategies: Choose the correct answer. (12 points: 4 points each)

13. When you compare two things, you show how they _____.
    a. are different
    b. sound when read aloud
    c. are spelled
    d. are similar

14. When you _____ two things, you show how they are different.
    a. punctuate
    b. compare
    c. contrast
    d. summarize

15. Juan and José are brothers. They share a bedroom. Juan's side of the bedroom is neat. José's side of the room is messy. Both boys have posters of their favorite basketball teams above their beds. How are Juan and José different?
    a. Juan is tall, and José is short.
    b. They have different hair colors.
    c. They sleep in separate bedrooms.
    d. Juan is neat, and José is messy.

D. ➤ Grammar/Usage: Choose the correct answer. (20 points: 4 points each)

16. _____ is the way language is put together.
    a. imagination
    b. genre
    c. grammar
    d. punctuation

17. The present continuous tense tells about something that _____.
    a. already happened
    b. will happen
    c. is happening now
    d. will never happen

18. Which sentence uses the present continuous tense?
    a. I will put that away.
    b. He is driving fast.
    c. They went to the movie.
    d. I did not eat my lunch.

19. Which sentence uses the present continuous tense?
    a. Esther did not play the piano.
    b. He should have done that yesterday.
    c. My dinner is cold.
    d. I am cooking dinner.

20. Priscilla _____ taking a break.
    a. am
    b. are
    c. did
    d. is

E. ➤ Writing (20 points)

Writing Prompt Write a personal narrative or poem about something your family does together. Use the words <u>I,</u> <u>me, we,</u> or <u>us</u> to write in the first-person point of view.

Grade

QUIZ Unit 1 • Chapter 2

A. ➤ Vocabulary: Choose the correct answer. (32 points: 4 points each)

1. Purr and meow are sounds that _____ make.
   a. horses
   b. cats
   c. snakes
   d. hamsters

2. A _____ is a sound that bears, lions, and dogs make.
   a. tweet
   b. hiss
   c. squeak
   d. growl

3. Which animal makes a hissing sound?
   a. elephant
   b. snake
   c. monkey
   d. cow

4. You can use a thesaurus or a synonym finder to find words that _____.
   a. have similar meanings
   b. are spelled the same
   c. are pronounced the same
   d. have opposite meanings

5. The horse galloped around the track and won the race. Another word for galloped is _____.
   a. drove
   b. looked
   c. limped
   d. ran

6. I took a large helping of my favorite vegetable at dinner. Another word for helping is _____.
   a. bag
   b. serving
   c. sniff
   d. mouthful

7. The band must rehearse twice a week. Another word for rehearse is _____.
   a. come
   b. music
   c. practice
   d. memorize

8. It is cold outside. I will wear my coat. Another word for coat is _____.
   a. tie
   b. sneakers
   c. jacket
   d. pajamas

B. ➤ Text Structure/Elements of Literature: Read and choose the correct answer. (12 points: 4 points each)

> "A Candle in the Window"
>
> 1   A long time ago, my grandfather was walking in the woods alone. He became lost. Suddenly, a snowstorm hit. My grandfather was very cold and could not see where he was going. He thought that he would freeze to death. But then, he saw a faint light in the distance. He walked toward the light and came to a small house. A candle was shining brightly in the window. He knocked at the door and was welcomed into the cozy home.
>
> 2   Now, on stormy nights, our family keeps a candle burning in the window. Hopefully, the candle will guide anyone who is lost to safety.

QUIZ Unit 1 • Chapter 2 (continued)

9. This reading is a ____.
   a. diary entry
   b. poem
   c. folktale
   d. play

10. The purpose of a writing is ____.
    a. why the author wrote it
    b. not important
    c. the same for all writings
    d. different each time it is read

11. The purpose of this writing is to ____.
    a. entertain
    b. persuade
    c. express an opinion
    d. present scientific information

C. ➤ Reading Strategies: Choose the correct answer. *(12 points: 4 points each)*

12. Reading aloud can help you ____ a selection.
    a. memorize
    b. forget
    c. copy
    d. understand

13. Every winter, Aunt Violet travels to Texas to see Uncle George. After a short visit, she travels to Florida to see her sister Estelle. Who does Aunt Violet visit in Texas?
    a. her daughters
    b. Uncle George
    c. Estelle's sister
    d. her sister

14. Everyone has a special place at our table. Father always sits at the head of the table, with Mother to his right. My brother and I sit across from Mother. Grandma sits next to mother.
    Where does Mother sit?
    a. at the head of the table
    b. next to Grandma
    c. next to the brother
    d. in front of Father

D. ➤ Grammar/Usage: Choose the correct answer. *(24 points: 4 points each)*

15. The ____ of the sentence is who or what the sentence is about.
    a. subject
    b. verb
    c. adjective
    d. pronoun

16. The ____ describes the action, or what happens in the sentence.
    a. subject   c. adjective
    b. verb   d. pronoun

17. The squirrel eats nuts. ____ is the subject of the sentence.
    a. The   c. eats
    b. squirrel   d. nuts

18. My sister sang at the party. ____ is the subject of the sentence.
    a. sister   c. the
    b. sang   d. party

19. His brother jogs every day. ____ is the verb in the sentence.
    a. His   c. jogs
    b. brother   d. day

20. Icicles dripped in the afternoon sun. ____ is the verb in the sentence.
    a. Icicles
    b. dripped
    c. afternoon
    d. sun

E. ➤ Writing *(20 points)*

Writing Prompt Think of a story you have heard at home. Write a narrative about this story.

QUIZ Unit 1 • Chapter 3

A. ➤ Vocabulary: Choose the correct answer. *(28 points: 4 points each)*

1. A _____ is a small red fruit.
   a. nut
   b. cranberry
   c. pumpkin
   d. feast

2. A pastry is a dessert. Pies are pastries. A _____ makes pastries.
   a. firefighter
   b. judge
   c. baker
   d. singer

3. An omelet is made of eggs, meat, and cheese. Most people eat omelets for _____.
   a. breakfast
   b. coffee break
   c. Christmas dinner
   d. bedtime snack

4. Ashley was very sorry for hurting her sister's feelings. Ashley was _____.
   a. joyful
   b. sorrowful
   c. wonderful
   d. grateful

5. They painted the room blue, green, pink, yellow, and white. It was very _____.
   a. careful
   b. bashful
   c. colorful
   d. thankful

6. The puppy loved to play. The puppy was _____.
   a. playful
   b. thankful
   c. careful
   d. sorrowful

7. Which word means cautious or full of care?
   a. cared
   b. care
   c. caring
   d. careful

B. ➤ Text Structure/Elements of Literature: Read and choose the correct answer. *(16 points: 4 points each)*

> "Family"
>
> 1 Just because we share a name,
>   Doesn't mean we're all the same.
>
> 2 I like movies and you like books.
>   Mother drives race cars while Father cooks.
>
> 3 On a favorite color we'll never agree,
>   I'm afraid a family we'll never be!
>
> 4 Oh, but being the same is not what a family's made of.
>   What makes a family is love!

8. Words with the same ending sound, such as books and cooks, _____.
   a. are opposites
   b. describe
   c. have the same meaning
   d. rhyme

9. Groups of lines in a poem are called _____.
   a. stanzas
   b. sentences
   c. entries
   d. paragraphs

10. Doesn't mean we're all the same. Which word rhymes with same?
   a. because
   b. name
   c. have
   d. mean

QUIZ Unit 1 • Chapter 3 (continued)

11. On a favorite color we'll never agree, I'm afraid a family we'll never be! Which words from the poem rhyme?
    a. favorite, agree
    b. family, favorite
    c. color, never
    d. agree, be

C. ➤ Reading Strategies: Choose the correct answer. (12 points: 4 points each)

12. The snowfall changed our neighborhood into a winter wonderland. It made everything white and clean. This writing helps you form a mental image of _____.
    a. a winter parade
    b. a city park
    c. snowy mountains
    d. the neighborhood

13. The circus brings a smile to every face. People gather in the colorful tent to watch the performers. Lion tamers, clowns, and elephants delight the crowd. This writing helps you form a mental image of _____.
    a. a birthday party
    b. the circus
    c. the zoo
    d. an amusement park

14. After the fire, the forest seemed lonely. The ground was black with ashes. Charcoal sticks stood where trees had been. This writing helps you form a mental image of _____.
    a. a meadow after the rain
    b. cooking with charcoal
    c. a forest after a fire
    d. cleaning the fireplace

D. ➤ Grammar/Usage: Choose the correct answer. (24 points: 4 points each)

15. My sister and I like our teachers. Choose a pronoun to replace the underlined words.
    a. Me   c. We
    b. She   d. He

16. Sampson ran all the way home. Choose a pronoun to replace the underlined word.
    a. I   c. They
    b. He   d. We

17. My grandparents travel south each winter. Choose a pronoun to replace the underlined words.
    a. I   c. We
    b. You   d. They

18. The book was a great gift. Choose a pronoun to replace the underlined words.
    a. It   c. You
    b. I   d. He

19. I will bake a cake. Which word is the subject pronoun?
    a. I   c. bake
    b. will   d. cake

20. You sang very well. Which word is the subject pronoun?
    a. You   c. very
    b. sang   d. well

E. ➤ Writing (20 points)

Writing Prompt Choose a favorite holiday and write a poem to describe it. Describe what you see, smell, and taste during your celebration. Use rhyming words.

QUIZ Unit 1 • Chapter 4

A. ➤ Vocabulary: Choose the correct answer. *(32 points: 4 points each)*

1. When I am done with my homework, I watch television. When do I watch television?
   a. before I do my homework
   b. after I do my homework
   c. during my homework
   d. I never watch television.

2. We are not allowed to talk during silent reading time. When is the room quiet?
   a. before silent reading time
   b. during silent reading time
   c. after silent reading time
   d. We have to be quiet all of the time.

3. I can't talk on the phone until I clean my room. I have to clean my room _____ I talk on the phone.
   a. after
   b. while
   c. if
   d. before

4. Hector will set the table. Then we will eat. When will we eat?
   a. while Hector sets the table
   b. after we wash the dishes
   c. before Hector sets the table
   d. after Hector sets the table

5. When your body temperature is too high, you have a <u>fever</u>. Then you may feel _____.
   a. fearful
   b. selfish
   c. beautiful
   d. feverish

6. I am learning to speak the language of <u>Sweden</u>. In other words, I am learning to speak _____.
   a. English
   b. Swedish
   c. French
   d. Latin

7. It was a rainy day. The clouds were <u>grayish</u>. Grayish means _____.
   a. sad
   b. cold
   c. a gray color
   d. fluffy

8. Justin is always thinking about himself. He doesn't care about others. Justin is _____.
   a. selfish
   b. careful
   c. thoughtful
   d. feverish

B. ➤ Text Structure/Elements of Literature: Read and choose the correct answer. *(16 points: 4 points each)*

"A Delicious Snack"

1   My brother says I make the best peanut butter and banana sandwiches. They are my favorite after-school snack. I will tell you how to make them. First, spread peanut butter on one slice of bread. Then, put banana slices on top of the peanut butter. Place the second slice of bread on top of the filling. After you have made your sandwich, cut it in half. Enjoy your snack.

---

9. A personal narrative is written _____.
   a. with a lot of adjectives
   b. like a mystery
   c. in first-person point of view
   d. about the past

10. What personal fact about the writer did you learn from this narrative?
    a. Peanut butter and banana sandwiches are his favorite snack.
    b. Sandwiches are good snacks.
    c. Bananas are sweet.
    d. Sandwiches should be cut in half.

QUIZ Unit 1 • Chapter 4 (continued)

11. This reading _____.
   a. describes different kinds of snacks
   b. gives instructions
   c. advertises a special sale
   d. lists things to remember

12. What do you do after the sandwich is made?
   a. Cut the crusts off.
   b. Spread the peanut butter.
   c. Slice the bananas.
   d. Cut the sandwich in half.

C. ➤ Reading Strategies: Choose the correct answer. (12 points: 4 points each)

13. Comparing what you read to your own experiences will help you to _____.
   a. understand what you read
   b. spell words
   c. write sentences
   d. read aloud

14. Marie felt her stomach tumble as she walked up the steps. She was always nervous on the first day of school. What question helps you compare your own experiences with Marie's?
   a. How do I feel on weekends?
   b. Why do I like summer?
   c. How do I feel on the first day of school?
   d. Why do I like school?

15. As Pedro crossed the finish line, a smile crossed his face. "I did it!" he yelled. What question helps you compare your own experiences with Pedro's?
   a. What is Pedro doing?
   b. When have I felt like Pedro?
   c. What makes me angry?
   d. What is my favorite sport?

D. ➤ Grammar/Usage: Choose the correct answer. (20 points: 4 points each)

16. A complement _____ the subject of a sentence.
   a. spells
   b. is the opposite of
   c. is nice to
   d. describes

17. That boy is my neighbor. What is the complement?
   a. boy
   b. is
   c. That
   d. neighbor

18. The leaves on the trees are green. What is the complement?
   a. The leaves
   b. green
   c. are
   d. the trees

19. My bedroom is messy. What does messy describe?
   a. me
   b. my bedroom
   c. my brother's room
   d. my handwriting

20. Stan, Elwin, and Darla are teenagers. What does teenagers describe?
   a. my classmates
   b. boys
   c. the neighbors
   d. Stan, Elwin, and Darla

E. ➤ Writing (20 points)

Writing Prompt Write a paragraph about what you like to do on the weekend. Use words that show time.

QUIZ Unit 1 • Chapter 5

A. ➤ Vocabulary: Choose the correct answer. *(24 points: 4 points each)*

1. The setting of a story is _____.
   a. the person who wrote the story
   b. the ending of the story
   c. when and where the story takes place
   d. the problem in the story

2. Jackson finished his test and gave it to his teacher. Then he waited for the bell to ring. The setting is _____.
   a. the zoo
   b. the kitchen
   c. a farm
   d. a classroom at school

3. Miguel spent most of his time watching the monkeys, but he also saw elephants and giraffes. The setting is _____.
   a. school
   b. a zoo
   c. a farm
   d. a pizza parlor

4. The words waiter, waitress, menu, order, and dinner are all related to _____.
   a. a doctor's office
   b. a dentist's office
   c. a motel
   d. a restaurant

5. I laughed when I heard the funny joke. What does the adjective funny describe?
   a. joke
   b. heard
   c. laughed
   d. when

6. Devin was looking for buried treasure. What does the adjective buried describe?
   a. Devin
   b. friends
   c. looking
   d. treasure

B. ➤ Text Structure/Elements of Literature: Read and choose the correct answer. *(24 points: 4 points each)*

"The Surprise Party"

1 "Surprise! Surprise! Happy Birthday!" Austin couldn't believe his eyes. A party for him?

2 "There must be over thirty people in my living room," he thought. Gifts were piled to the ceiling. A huge cake was on the table. His face beamed as he surveyed the guests. His parents, teachers, relatives, and friends were all there. Everyone had come to celebrate his birthday.

---

7. From "The Surprise Party," you can tell that _____.
   a. Austin does not have many friends
   b. Austin has three sisters
   c. Other people like Austin.
   d. Austin gets good grades in school

8. Austin couldn't believe his eyes. Austin was _____.
   a. scared
   b. tired
   c. upset
   d. surprised

9. His face beamed as he surveyed the guests. Austin _____.
   a. smiled
   b. went to bed
   c. cried
   d. frowned

10. A story that fills a book is a _____.
   a. novel
   b. journal
   c. narrative
   d. diary

QUIZ Unit 1 • Chapter 5 *(continued)*

11. If a story really happened, but it did not happen exactly the way the author wrote it, we say the story is _____.
    a. a lie
    b. a true story
    c. based on a true story
    d. pretend

12. When a story is made up, it is _____.
    a. nonfiction
    b. a first-person narrative
    c. a historical narrative
    d. fiction

C. ➤ Reading Strategies: Choose the correct answer. *(16 points: 4 points each)*

13. The reason something happens is the _____.
    a. cause
    b. because
    c. punctuation
    d. effect

14. I didn't sleep well because I was nervous about the big race. The underlined phrase is the _____.
    a. strategy
    b. cause
    c. connection
    d. effect

15. Mother was angry because I didn't do the dishes. Which is the effect?
    a. Mother was angry
    b. Mother was angry because
    c. I didn't do the dishes
    d. the dishes

16. I was hungry because I skipped breakfast. Which is the cause?
    a. I was hungry
    b. I was hungry because
    c. I skipped breakfast
    d. breakfast

D. ➤ Grammar/Usage: Choose the correct answer. *(16 points: 4 points each)*

17. A possessive noun _____.
    a. shows who has something
    b. is the solution
    c. describes the action
    d. is the verb

18. A singular noun _____.
    a. stands for one person or thing
    b. is two or more people
    c. states the problem
    d. describes a person's behavior

19. Our teacher's smile warms the room. The underlined word is a(an) _____.
    a. verb
    b. possessive noun
    c. phrase
    d. adjective

20. The dog's paws were like large, furry hammers. Which word is a singular noun?
    a. dog's
    b. paws
    c. furry
    d. hammers

E. ➤ Writing *(20 points)*

Writing Prompt Write a fictional narrative about an event that might happen in class. Use possessive nouns.

TEST • Unit 1

A. ➤ Reading

The Letter

1   Today is not going well. That's
because yesterday Papa said, "Samuel,
tomorrow you must write to your
grandparents. It has been weeks since
they heard from you!" He was really
annoyed.

2   I don't have a single word on the
paper. All I do is scribble little pictures
in the margins. I know that my
teenaged sister writes them almost
every week. Well, at least one of their
grandchildren is thoughtful.

3   Here's my problem. My family and I have been in our
new home for one year. We are all thankful to be here. We
have new friends, new things, and a new life. But if I tell
this to my grandparents, they will think I don't miss them.

4   I do remember the wonderful times we had together.
Over my desk is a map of the Dominican Republic. My
grandparents' town is on a river. I can even point to the
places where Grandfather took us in his sailboat.

5   Look! I drew a picture of each thing I was thinking
about. There's one of Grandfather's sailboat. There's even
one of his sister, my Great Aunt Carmen. Now I know what
to write! I will say what each picture means to me. Then I
will mail the letter, and my grandparents will get a big
surprise.

My Notes

Example notes:

Papa annoyed

Must write to grandparents

TEST • Unit 1 (continued)

B. ➤ Reading Comprehension: Choose the correct answer. *(20 points: 2 points each)*

1. When did Papa speak to Samuel about writing a letter?
   a. last week
   b. yesterday
   c. today
   d. tomorrow

2. Samuel was writing to his ____.
   a. friend
   b. Papa
   c. grandparents
   d. great aunt

3. What trouble is Samuel having with his letter?
   a. He does not know what to write.
   b. He does not know how to draw.
   c. He does not know where to send the letter.
   d. He does not have any paper.

4. When does Samuel's sister write letters to her grandparents?
   a. every year
   b. once a month
   c. almost every week
   d. at least every day

5. The picture of the sailboat in the reading best represents ____.
   a. where Samuel's family now lives
   b. Samuel's wish to sail on the ocean
   c. one thing Samuel asks his grandparents to do during their visit
   d. a special time shared by Samuel and his grandfather

6. How does Samuel feel about where he lives?
   a. He likes his new home.
   b. He wants to look for a different home.
   c. He is afraid of his new home.
   d. He does not like his new home.

7. Samuel tries to avoid telling his grandparents about his new life because ____.
   a. he wants his grandparents to come stay with his family
   b. he does not want his grandparents to think that he does not miss them
   c. he hopes his parents will tell his grandparents for him
   d. he loves his grandparents

8. Where do Samuel's grandparents live?
   a. with Samuel
   b. in the United States
   c. in the Dominican Republic
   d. next door to Samuel

9. Where does Samuel keep his map?
   a. over his bed
   b. over his desk
   c. under his bed
   d. in his closet

10. Which of these is something Samuel enjoyed doing with his grandfather?
   a. riding bicycles
   b. going on picnics
   c. playing basketball
   d. sailing on his sailboat

TEST • Unit 1 *(continued)*

C. ➤ **Reading Strategies:** Choose the correct answer. *(10 points: 2 points each)*

11. How is Samuel's sister different from Samuel?
  a. She did not move away.
  b. She writes to her grandparents almost every week.
  c. She is happy in her new home.
  d. She draws great pictures.

12. All I do is scribble little pictures in the margins. This sentence helps you form a mental image of _____.
  a. what Samuel's paper looks like
  b. the pictures Samuel has drawn
  c. Samuel's family
  d. Samuel's grandparents

13. Which of the following events would help you relate your experience to Samuel's experience?
  a. breaking a window
  b. reading a good book
  c. writing a letter
  d. watching a movie

14. Samuel's day is not going well. What is the cause of Samuel's bad day?
  a. Papa is annoyed.
  b. Samuel's sister is thoughtful.
  c. Samuel's grandparents are coming to visit.
  d. Samuel has to write a letter.

15. Samuel drew pictures on his paper because _____.
  a. he did not know how to spell
  b. he did not know what to write
  c. his father told him to
  d. he is an artist

D. ➤ **Elements of Literature:** Choose the correct answer. *(10 points: 2 points each)*

16. Who is the narrator in this story?
  a. Papa
  b. Grandfather
  c. Samuel's sister
  d. Samuel

17. What is the narrator telling the reader about?
  a. his own experience
  b. his friends
  c. something that happened in history
  d. scientific information

18. The purpose of this reading is to _____.
  a. entertain
  b. express an opinion
  c. persuade
  d. record history

19. My family and I have been in our new home for one <u>year</u>. We are all thankful to be <u>here</u>. The underlined words in the sentences are _____.
  a. synonyms
  b. antonyms
  c. rhyming words
  d. adjectives

20. But if I tell this to my grandparents, they will think I don't miss them. This sentence tells you that _____.
  a. Samuel does not want to hurt his grandparent's feelings
  b. Samuel is angry
  c. Samuel is excited
  d. Samuel does not care about his grandparents

TEST • Unit 1 *(continued)*

E. ➤ **Vocabulary:** Choose the correct answer. *(10 points: 2 points each)*

21. Who is Papa?
    a. Great Aunt Carmen's father
    b. Grandfather's father
    c. Samuel's sister
    d. Samuel's father

22. He was really annoyed. Another word for annoyed is ____.
    a. happy
    b. upset
    c. tired
    d. puzzled

23. We are all thankful to be here. Thankful means ____.
    a. full of thanks
    b. they said thank you to each other
    c. they do not like it here
    d. they wish they were here

24. Then I will mail the letter, and my grandparents will get a big surprise. The word surprise shows that Samuel's grandparents will be ____.
    a. saddened by Samuel's writing
    b. amazed to receive the letter
    c. too tired to read the letter
    d. worried about the letter

25. When will Samuel mail his letter?
    a. before he draws the pictures
    b. after his father reads the letter
    c. after he writes about each picture
    d. before he rides on Grandfather's sailboat

F. ➤ **Grammar/Usage** *(10 points: 2 points each)*

26. Today is not going well. This sentence is in the ____.
    a. present continuous tense
    b. first person
    c. past tense
    d. future tense

27. My family and I have been in our new home for one year. The underlined phrase is the ____.
    a. verb
    b. problem
    c. subject
    d. solution

28. Oscar is my best friend. He lives next door to me. He refers to ____.
    a. Oscar
    b. my
    c. best
    d. me

29. Rita is very intelligent. What is the complement in the sentence?
    a. Rita
    b. is
    c. very
    d. intelligent

30. This is Raphael's new game. What is the possessive noun in this sentence?
    a. This
    b. new
    c. Raphael's
    d. game

TEST • Unit 1 (continued)

G. ➤ Writing Conventions: Choose the correct answer. *(10 points: 2 points each)*

31. <u>Grandfather</u> and I went to the city today. Why is <u>Grandfather</u> capitalized?
    a. It is being used as a name.
    b. It is the name of a city.
    c. It is the title of the reading.
    d. It is at the beginning of the sentence.

32. Which sentence is punctuated correctly?
    a. Watch out for that car,
    b. Mabel said let's go.
    c. Tony is eating lunch.
    d. Are you going to the store.

33. Liza and i are partners on this art project. Which word needs to be capitalized in the sentence?
    a. i
    b. partners
    c. art
    d. project

34. Roya is from <u>Mexico</u>. <u>Mexico</u> is capitalized because _____.
    a. it is at the end of the sentence
    b. it is a person's name
    c. it is a book title
    d. it is a country

35. I <u>do not</u> have time to rest before leaving. What is another way to write <u>do not</u>?
    a. don't
    b. can't
    c. didn't
    d. won't

H. ➤ Editing: Read and choose the correct answer. *(10 points: 2 points each)*

(1) Dear Aunt Laurie,

(2) Mother said I should <u>wrote</u> to cheer you up. (3) I'm sorry you twisted you're ankle. (4) Where I twisted my ankle, I got to stay home from school for three days. (5) Do you get to stay home from work! (6) How did your leg feel now? (7) Write back soon.

(8) Your nephew,
(9) Lukas

36. In sentence 2, the word <u>wrote</u> should be changed to _____.
    a. wroten
    b. write
    c. writed
    d. writing

37. What change should you make to sentence 3?
    a. change *I'm* to *I*
    b. change *twisted* to *twisting*
    c. change *you're* to *your*
    d. make no change

38. What change should you make to sentence 4?
    a. change *Where* to *When*
    b. change *twisted* to *twist*
    c. change *my* to *mine*
    d. make no change

39. What change should you make to sentence 5?
    a. change *Do* to *Are*
    b. change the exclamation point to a period
    c. change the exclamation point to a question mark
    d. make no change

TEST • Unit 1 (continued)

40. What change should you make to sentence 6?
- **a.** change *How* to *Who*
- **b.** change *did* to *does*
- **c.** change *your* to *you're*
- **d.** make no change

I. ➤ **Writing** (20 points)

> **Writing Prompt** Write a narrative about a tradition that is shared by your family or culture. Use words to show mental images of the sights and sounds of your tradition. Use the Planning Guide to help you write.

Planning Guide
- ❏ Ask yourself these questions:
    - **a.** What tradition does my family or culture share?
    - **b.** What words will help others to picture this tradition?
- ❏ Use the answers to these questions to write your narrative.
- ❏ Proofread your narrative for spelling, capitalization, and punctuation.

Name _____ Date _____

Grade

QUIZ Unit 2 • Chapter 1

A. ➤ Vocabulary: Choose the correct answer. *(24 points: 4 points each)*

1. The _____ of a word is the other words around it that help give it meaning.
   a. origin
   b. context
   c. sound
   d. letters

2. Anica <u>adores</u> her cat. She hugs and kisses it everyday. <u>Adore</u> means _____.
   a. ignore
   b. wash
   c. love
   d. feed

3. The <u>gust</u> of wind blew leaves all over the yard. A <u>gust</u> is a _____.
   a. strong breeze
   b. tree branch
   c. tornado
   d. hurricane

4. A word's _____ is where it comes from.
   a. sound
   b. look
   c. letters
   d. origin

5. The _____ on a cactus can be very sharp.
   a. blazes
   b. basks
   c. spines
   d. bark

6. A hare is most similar to a _____.
   a. snake
   b. rabbit
   c. lizard
   d. roadrunner

B. ➤ Text Structure/Elements of Literature: Read and choose the correct answer. *(32 points: 4 points each)*

> "Ode to My Dog," by Andres
>
> 1   You are loving
>   You are kind
>   You make me smile
>   Buddy, you are my best friend.
>
> 2   You bring me joy
>   You make me happy
>   You love me
>   Buddy, you are my best friend.

7. "Ode to My Dog" is a(n) _____.
   a. poem
   b. fairytale
   c. informational text
   d. autobiography

8. "Ode to My Dog" is mostly about a _____.
   a. horse
   b. game
   c. park
   d. dog

9. What does Andres call Buddy?
   a. his friend
   b. his cat
   c. his dog
   d. his bicycle

10. How does Buddy make Andres feel?
    a. sleepy
    b. happy
    c. hungry
    d. angry

QUIZ Unit 2 • Chapter 1 (continued)

11. Poetry that does not rhyme is called
    ____.
    a. verse
    b. meter
    c. iambic pentameter
    d. free verse

12. What type of poetry is "Ode to My Dog"?
    a. verse
    b. rhyming
    c. iambic pentameter
    d. free verse

13. ____ words sound alike.
    a. Adverbial
    b. Rhyming
    c. Suffix
    d. Prefix

14. Call and ____ are rhyming words.
    a. tree
    b. ball
    c. leaf
    d. seat

C. ➤ Reading Strategies: Choose the correct answer. *(12 points: 4 points each)*

15. ____ are pictures that writers create with words.
    a. Similes
    b. Metaphors
    c. Images
    d. Personification

16. Grandma's house is white. Which word helps you picture Grandma's house?
    a. white
    b. Grandma
    c. is
    d. house

17. Adolfo has a red bicycle. Which word helps you picture Adolfo's bicycle?
    a. Adolfo
    b. has
    c. a
    d. red

D. ➤ Grammar/Usage: Choose the correct answer. *(12 points: 4 points each)*

18. Simple ____ tense is used to talk about something that happens regularly.
    a. adverb
    b. present
    c. past
    d. future

19. Which sentence is in the simple present tense?
    a. We are studying together after school.
    b. We studied together after school.
    c. We have studied together after school.
    d. We study together after school.

20. Which sentence is correct?
    a. Carla goes to school every day.
    b. Carla goes to school yesterday.
    c. Carla going to school every day.
    d. Carla go to school every day.

E. ➤ Writing *(20 points)*

Writing Prompt Choose your favorite season. List six characteristics of that season. Use your list to write a free verse poem about the season.

QUIZ Unit 2 • Chapter 2

A. ➤ Vocabulary: Choose the correct answer. *(24 points: 4 points each)*

1. Taking _____ while reading is a way to identify words that you don't understand.
   a. essays
   b. papers
   c. notes
   d. stories

2. Learning new words is a way to _____ vocabulary.
   a. look up
   b. meet
   c. build
   d. write

3. A _____ is a group of letters added to the beginning of a word.
   a. prefix
   b. suffix
   c. noun
   d. verb

4. The subway is an easy way to travel. The prefix in subway is _____.
   a. origin
   b. su
   c. sub
   d. way

5. A subtitle goes _____ the main title of a book.
   a. next to
   b. below
   c. above
   d. behind

6. The dog went unnoticed behind the tree. The prefix in unnoticed is _____.
   a. notice
   b. ed
   c. un
   d. noticed

B. ➤ Text Structure/Elements of Literature: Read and choose the correct answer. *(32 points: 4 points each)*

"Teacher of the Year"

1 GUADALUPE: How long have you been a teacher, Mrs. Lopez?

2 MRS. LOPEZ: I've been teaching for fifteen years.

3 GUADALUPE: What do you like most about teaching?

4 MRS. LOPEZ: Well, I love young people and I have great students.

5 GUADALUPE: What subject do you teach?

6 MRS. LOPEZ: I teach science.

7 GUADALUPE: What will you do during this summer vacation?

8 MRS. LOPEZ: My husband and I will travel to Mexico to visit our families.

---

7. "Teacher of the Year" is a(n) _____.
   a. poem
   b. interview
   c. informational text
   d. short story

8. In "Teacher of the Year," who is the interviewer?
   a. Science
   b. Mrs. Lopez's husband
   c. Mexico
   d. Guadalupe

QUIZ Unit 2 • Chapter 2 (continued)

9. In "Teacher of the Year," who is the interviewee?
   a. science students
   b. vacationers
   c. Mrs. Lopez
   d. family members

10. Where will Mrs. Lopez travel during her summer vacation?
   a. to Mexico
   b. to her home
   c. to the store
   d. to the mall

11. _____ is why characters act the way they do.
   a. Mood
   b. Motivation
   c. Irony
   d. Imagery

12. What motivates Mrs. Lopez to teach?
   a. She likes to travel.
   b. She is going to Mexico.
   c. She teaches science.
   d. She likes young people.

13. Why is Mrs. Lopez going to Mexico?
   a. to be warm
   b. to see snow falling
   c. to learn Spanish
   d. to visit her family

14. Mrs. Lopez thinks _____ are great.
   a. her students
   b. vacations
   c. families
   d. teachers

C. ➤ Reading Strategies: Choose the correct answer. (12 points: 4 points each)

15. Information that is true is a(n) _____.
   a. lie
   b. fact
   c. opinion
   d. assumption

16. A(n) _____ is what someone thinks about something.
   a. opinion
   b. fact
   c. lie
   d. report

17. Eldora believes that blue is the prettiest color. This statement is a(n) _____.
   a. fact
   b. past tense statement
   c. opinion
   d. visual

D. ➤ Grammar/Usage: Choose the correct answer. (12 points: 4 points each)

18. What punctuation is used at the end of a question?
   a. an exclamation mark
   b. a question mark
   c. a period
   d. a comma

19. How is a question _____.
   a. effect
   b. adverb
   c. prefix
   d. word

20. Which of these is a question word?
   a. why
   b. is
   c. because
   d. however

E. ➤ Writing (20 points)

> **Writing Prompt** Choose one of your teachers to interview. Tell why you chose this teacher and write five questions to ask during the interview.

QUIZ Unit 2 • Chapter 3

A. ➤ **Vocabulary:** Choose the correct answer. *(24 points: 4 points each)*

1. _____ is the information that surrounds a word.
   a. Synonym
   b. Context
   c. Homophone
   d. Paragraph

2. Geraldo was <u>freezing</u> because he had left his coat at home. <u>Freezing</u> means _____.
   a. cold
   b. hot
   c. scared
   d. tired

3. Ines has a <u>cheerful</u> personality and she's always smiling. <u>Cheerful</u> means _____.
   a. painful
   b. angry
   c. happy
   d. sad

4. _____ are words that sound alike but have different meanings.
   a. Nouns
   b. Verbs
   c. Suffixes
   d. Homonyms

5. Gitana went downtown to <u>see</u> the parade. Which of these is a homonym of <u>see</u>?
   a. saw
   b. sea
   c. site
   d. seat

6. José is going <u>to</u> be late for school because he overslept. Which of these is a homonym of <u>to</u>?
   a. two
   b. true
   c. ten
   d. through

B. ➤ **Text Structure/Elements of Literature:** Read and choose the correct answer. *(32 points: 4 points each)*

"Damita's Valuable Lesson"

1   Damita's mother told her she could go out with her friends after she did her chores. Damita decided to do her chores after she watched her favorite television show. Homer, Damita's parrot, said, "Damita, you should do your chores now so you can go out with your friends." However, Damita didn't listen. Homer became angry with her. After the show ended, Damita took a nap. When she awoke, four hours later, it was very late. Because Damita waited too long to do her chores, she could not go out with her friends.

---

7. "Damita's Valuable Lesson" is a(n) _____.
   a. poem
   b. interview
   c. fable
   d. personal narrative

8. In "Damita's Valuable Lesson," what does Damita want to do?
   a. go out with her friends
   b. do homework
   c. go shopping
   d. her chores

QUIZ Unit 2 • Chapter 3 *(continued)*

9. In "Damita's Valuable Lesson," what is the first thing Damita does?
   a. takes a nap
   b. goes out with her friends
   c. plays the piano
   d. watches television

10. Why is Damita unable to go out?
    a. She does her homework too quickly.
    b. She burns the family dinner.
    c. She waits too long to do her chores.
    d. She walks her dog in the snow.

11. When an author gives animals human thoughts, feelings, and actions, this is called _____.
    a. simile
    b. metaphor
    c. imagery
    d. personification

12. What does Homer tell Damita?
    a. to do her chores before it gets too late
    b. to go get dinner for the family
    c. to feed him because he is hungry
    d. to wash him because he is dirty

13. How does Homer feel when Damita refuses to listen to him?
    a. hungry
    b. angry
    c. tired
    d. sad

14. In "Damita's Valuable Lesson," what human quality does Homer have?
    a. the ability to dance
    b. the ability to cook
    c. the ability to speak
    d. the ability to paint

C. ➤ **Reading Strategies:** Choose the correct answer. *(12 points: 4 points each)*

15. The most important idea in a story is the _____ idea.
    a. short   c. main
    b. long   d. minor

16. A(n) _____ is an example, explanation, or event that supports the main idea.
    a. synonym   c. effect
    b. detail   d. cause

17. Rosalinda is a good swimmer. Which detail supports this sentence?
    a. She has a new bathing suit.
    b. She won the essay contest.
    c. She won a swimming competition.
    d. She likes to play sports.

D. ➤ **Grammar/Usage:** Choose the correct answer. *(12 points: 4 points each)*

18. She loves to read books. Which word is the subject pronoun?
    a. She   c. to read
    b. loves   d. books

19. Enrico rode his bicycle with them. Which word is the object pronoun?
    a. rode   c. bicycles
    b. his   d. them

20. The teacher will take his students to the library. Which pronoun can replace the underlined words?
    a. she   c. they
    b. them   d. its

E. ➤ **Writing** *(20 points)*

Writing Prompt Think about a time when you learned a lesson. Write a fable to describe what you learned.

QUIZ Unit 2 • Chapter 4

A. ➤ **Vocabulary:** Choose the correct answer. *(24 points: 4 points each)*

1. Word _____ can help you remember the meanings of new words.
   a. squares
   b. triangles
   c. circles
   d. pentagons

2. One activity in a word square is to write a _____ using the new word.
   a. story
   b. sentence
   c. report
   d. paragraph

3. A _____ combines two words into one.
   a. multiple-meaning word
   b. vivid word
   c. homonym
   d. compound word

4. Which of these is a compound word?
   a. bus
   b. mailbox
   c. snowing
   d. books

5. Which of these is a compound word?
   a. notebook
   b. water
   c. lovely
   d. telephone

6. We eat pancakes every morning. Which word is a compound word?
   a. eat
   b. pancakes
   c. every
   d. morning

B. ➤ **Text Structure/Elements of Literature:** Read and choose the correct answer. *(32 points: 4 points each)*

> "Lola's Special Treat"
>
> 1   Lola was the youngest of three girls. Her sisters, Elisa and Juanita, were going to the movies. Lola begged them to take her, but they said that she was too young to go. Lola started to cry when they left the house. So Lola's mother took Lola out for ice cream and a movie. Lola had a lot of fun with her mother and was glad that she hadn't followed her sisters.

7. "Lola's Special Treat" is a _____.
   a. poem
   b. fictional narrative
   c. biography
   d. drama

8. In "Lola's Special Treat," what does Lola want to do with her sisters?
   a. eat pizza
   b. wash dishes
   c. go to the movies
   d. play ball

9. In "Lola's Special Treat," what does Lola's mother do with Lola?
   a. watches television
   b. goes out for ice cream
   c. works in the garden
   d. writes letters to friends

10. Lola has a _____ time with her mother.
    a. good
    b. bad
    c. boring
    d. messy

QUIZ Unit 2 • Chapter 4 *(continued)*

11. The message that an author wants readers to get from a reading is the _____.
a. theme
b. title
c. point of view
d. setting

12. A _____ is a detail in the story that helps readers find the theme.
a. character
b. narrator
c. clue
d. setting

13. What is the theme of "Lola's Special Treat"?
a. Big sisters go to the movies with friends.
b. Girls can have fun with their mothers.
c. It is fun to go out for ice cream and movies.
d. It is hard for some sisters to get along.

14. In "Lola's Special Treat," what is a clue to the story's theme?
a. Lola asks her mother for a video game.
b. Lola cries until her sisters return.
c. Lola follows her sisters.
d. Lola ends up having fun with her mother.

C. ➤ Reading Strategies: Choose the correct answer. *(12 points: 4 points each)*

15. You come to a(n) _____ after you decide that something is true or not true.
a. introduction
b. stop
c. conclusion
d. detail

16. A reader draws conclusions after thinking carefully about the _____.
a. title
b. structure
c. facts
d. length

17. Zora loves bright colors. You can draw the conclusion that Zora likes the color _____.
a. black
b. gray
c. yellow
d. brown

D. ➤ Grammar/Usage: Choose the correct answer. *(12 points: 4 points each)*

18. A(n) _____ describes a noun.
a. adjective
b. verb
c. antonym
d. prefix

19. Tia is fifteen years old. Leo is seventeen years old. Leo is _____ than Tia.
a. oldest
b. more old
c. older
d. old

20. My opinion is that dogs are _____ than cats.
a. most intelligent
b. more intelligent
c. intelligenter
d. intelligent

E. ➤ Writing *(20 points)*

Writing Prompt Write a paragraph about a fictional character who learns that studying can help him or her get better grades.

QUIZ Unit 2 • Chapter 5

A. ➤ Vocabulary: Choose the correct answer. *(24 points: 4 points each)*

1. _____ help the reader identify vocabulary words.
   a. Illustrations
   b. Text features
   c. Page numbers
   d. Genres

2. The word *camera* uses the text feature known as _____.
   a. boldface
   b. underline
   c. italics
   d. bullets

3. The word **watch** uses the text feature known as _____.
   a. boldface
   b. underline
   c. italics
   d. bullets

4. A word's _____ is where a word came from.
   a. clue
   b. web
   c. strategy
   d. origin

5. A <u>genre</u> is a type of writing. The origin of <u>genre is</u> _____.
   a. English
   b. Spanish
   c. Hmong
   d. French

6. Many _____ words are borrowed from other languages and cultures.
   a. origin
   b. strategy
   c. English
   d. boldface

B. ➤ Text Structure/Elements of Literature: Read and choose the correct answer. *(32 points: 4 points each)*

"Boomers, Flyers, and Joeys"

1   Kangaroos are mostly found in Australia. Male kangaroos are called *boomers*. Female kangaroos are called *flyers*. Baby kangaroos are known as *joeys*. Kangaroos are marsupial mammals. This means that females carry their babies in stomach pouches and feed them milk. Kangaroos move by hopping and can jump over things that are ten feet (3.0 m) high. They eat grass. They can go for months without drinking water. The largest kangaroo is the red kangaroo. It is the largest marsupial in the world.

---

7. "Boomers, Flyers, and Joeys" is a(n) _____.
   a. fable
   b. narrative fiction
   c. informational text
   d. interview

8. In "Boomers, Flyers, and Joeys," what are female kangaroos called?
   a. boomers
   b. flyers
   c. joeys
   d. small

9. What is "Boomers, Flyers, and Joeys" mostly about?
   a. kangaroos
   b. giraffes
   c. lions
   d. bears

QUIZ Unit 2 • Chapter 5 (continued)

10. What do kangaroos eat?
    a. marsupials
    b. water
    c. other animals
    d. grass

11. Visuals are _____.
    a. indexes
    b. table of contents
    c. pictures and graphic organizers
    d. paragraphs

12. Which visual would help you picture "Boomers, Flyers, and Joeys"?
    a. a picture of a tree
    b. a picture of kangaroos
    c. a picture of a house
    d. a picture of cars

13. What would help you visualize a kangaroo's food?
    a. a picture of grass
    b. a picture of a kangaroo
    c. a picture of a flower
    d. a picture of Australia

14. What would help you visualize the largest kangaroo?
    a. a picture of a marsupial
    b. a picture of a joey
    c. a picture of a hill
    d. a picture of a red kangaroo

C. ➤ **Reading Strategies:** Choose the correct answer. *(12 points: 4 points each)*

15. Making a(n) _____ of an informational text helps you organize and remember what you read.
    a. copy
    b. outline
    c. conclusion
    d. illustration

16. A _____ is usually at the top of an outline.
    a. topic
    b. subtopic
    c. dialogue
    d. detail

17. In outlines, subtopics are described using _____.
    a. imagery
    b. figurative language
    c. details
    d. predictions

D. ➤ **Grammar/Usage:** Choose the correct answer. *(12 points: 4 points each)*

18. The kangaroo hopped over the wall. _____ is the verb.
    a. Kangaroo
    b. Hopped
    c. Over
    d. Wall

19. The large dog barked. _____ is the verb.
    a. The
    b. Large
    c. Dog
    d. Barked

20. The sun shone brightly. _____ is the subject.
    a. The
    b. Sun
    c. Shone
    d. Brightly

E. ➤ **Writing** *(20 points)*

Writing Prompt Write an informational paragraph about your favorite book. Tell the title, the author, and about the characters in the book. Explain why the book is your favorite.

TEST • Unit 2

A. ➤ Reading

Why The Chipmunk Has Stripes

1 Once upon a time, long ago, all the animals gathered for a great meeting. They had a very important question to decide. Should it be daylight all the time, or should it be night?

2 Bear stood up on his hind legs, rumbling in a big, deep voice, "Always night! Always night!"

3 Chipmunk became angry. "You can talk all you like," he squeaked in his tiny voice, "but daylight will come whether you want it or not."

4 The other animals did not pay attention to Chipmunk but went on roaring and growling in disagreement. Chipmunk danced around, squeaking, "The sun will come up when she wants to! The sun will go down when she wants to!"

5 And before the animals knew it, a pale light shone in the sky, and the golden sun rose above the trees. Could it be possible that it was daylight whether they wanted it to be or not?

6 A squeaky voice suddenly called out of the crowd. "What did I tell . . . "

7 "GRRRR!" Chipmunk ran through the trees with Bear chasing after him. Luckily, Chipmunk was faster. He slipped into a hole in a tree before Bear could catch him. But, just before he disappeared, Bear tried to grab him with his big paw. The black stripes on the Chipmunk's back today show where Bear's claws scratched him that night long ago.

TEST • Unit 2 (continued)

B. ➤ **Reading Comprehension:** Choose the correct answer. *(20 points: 2 points each)*

1. "Why The Chipmunk Has Stripes" is a(n) _____.
   a. novel
   b. fable
   c. interview
   d. informational text

2. A fable is written to _____.
   a. teach a lesson
   b. show a process
   c. inform readers
   d. persuade readers

3. "Why The Chipmunk Has Stripes" is mostly about the _____.
   a. sun
   b. stars
   c. chipmunk
   d. food chain

4. The chipmunk keeps saying that the _____ will rise and set when she wants to.
   a. moon
   b. wave
   c. star
   d. sun

5. In "Why The Chipmunk Has Stripes," the animals gathered for a _____.
   a. meeting
   b. feast
   c. suntan
   d. dance

6. How does Bear feel when Chipmunk says that animals can not control day or night?
   a. glad
   b. angry
   c. sad
   d. surprised

7. At the end of the story, who growls, "GRRRR"?
   a. Bear
   b. Chipmunk
   c. the other animals
   d. the sun

8. Bear wants it to be _____ all the time.
   a. dinner time
   b. quiet
   c. day
   d. night

9. How do the other animals treat Chipmunk?
   a. They step on him.
   b. They do not listen to him.
   c. They listen to him.
   d. They love him.

10. What does Chipmunk do in the last paragraph?
    a. slips into a hole
    b. falls asleep
    c. comes to the meeting
    d. plays with Bear

TEST • Unit 2 (continued)

C. ➤ **Reading Strategies:** Choose the correct answer. *(10 points: 2 points each)*

11. The information in paragraph 7 helps you to picture _____.
    a. how Bear got big paws
    b. how Chipmunk got stripes on his back
    c. why animals like to meet in the forest
    d. why the sun only shines during the day

12. The animals in the story act like humans. What does this show about the story?
    a. It is about the environment.
    b. The sun is not happy.
    c. The author uses personification.
    d. It is about how the sun rises.

13. What is the main idea of paragraph 1?
    a. The animals had many parties.
    b. The animals liked to dance.
    c. The animals decided something.
    d. The animals had a meeting.

14. From the story, you can conclude that _____.
    a. Bear and Chipmunk do not get along
    b. Bear is friendly toward Chipmunk
    c. the animals don't like Bear
    d. all of the animals like Chipmunk

15. Which of the following would be a major heading in an outline of this story?
    a. Bears have deep voices.
    b. Bear becomes angry with Chipmunk.
    c. The sun only comes out at night.
    d. The moon is part of the night sky.

D. ➤ **Elements of Literature:** Choose the correct answer. *(10 points: 2 points each)*

16. The sun in the story is an example of personification because _____.
    a. the animals show respect to it
    b. it is breathing
    c. the writer refers to it as "she"
    d. it occasionally runs around Earth

17. What is Bear's motive for repeating the words *Always night*?
    a. He knows it is late and does not want to go to sleep.
    b. He wants the animals to decide that it should be night all of the time.
    c. He likes to say this phrase.
    d. He says what all of the other animals are thinking.

18. Which of the following visuals would best help you picture the animals' meeting?
    a. A picture of the animals grouped together discussing something.
    b. A picture of the animals looking for a place to have their meeting.
    c. A chart showing what each of the animals likes to hunt and eat.
    d. A map of the forest where the animals live.

19. Which describes the theme of this story?
    a. The forest is full of wonderful and amazing animals.
    b. Animals solve problems when no one is looking.
    c. Daylight is better than the night sky.
    d. There are some things that we cannot control.

20. A poem about "Why The Chipmunk Has Stripes" that has no rhyming words would be called _____.
    a. free verse
    b. a rhyme
    c. verse
    d. stanza

TEST • Unit 2 *(continued)*

E. ➤ Vocabulary: Choose the correct answer. *(10 points: 2 points each)*

21. In paragraph 3, squeaked means _____.
    a. said in a loud, deep voice
    b. ran up a tree
    c. jumped very high
    d. said in a high, quiet voice

22. "Why The Chipmunk Has Stripes" explains _____.
    a. why animals prefer to live in the forest
    b. why the chipmunk looks the way it does
    c. which animal is the bravest
    d. how the chipmunk became a fast runner

23. In paragraph 3, the word daylight is a(n) _____.
    a. synonym
    b. antonym
    c. compound word
    d. contraction

24. Bear's claws made the stripes on Chipmunk's back. Which word fits on a word square for claw?
    a. food
    b. tooth
    c. person
    d. animal

25. He slipped into a hole. In this sentence, slip means "to go into." Slip can also mean _____.
    a. sleep
    b. fall
    c. cry
    d. dance

F. ➤ Grammar/Usage: Choose the correct answer. *(10 points: 2 points each)*

26. The rabbit is quicker than the turtle. What is the comparative adjective in the sentence?
    a. rabbit
    b. is
    c. than
    d. quicker

27. What punctuation mark goes at the end of a question?
    a. a period
    b. a question mark
    c. a comma
    d. an exclamation point

28. Tomas went for a walk. What is the subject of this sentence?
    a. Tomas
    b. went
    c. for
    d. walk

29. Carmen writes a letter to her cousin. What is the verb in the sentence?
    a. Carmen
    b. writes
    c. letter
    d. cousin

30. Melanie tossed it to Lily. What is the object pronoun of the sentence?
    a. Melanie
    b. tossed
    c. it
    d. him

TEST • Unit 2 *(continued)*

G. ➤ Writing Conventions: Choose the correct answer. *(10 points: 2 points each)*

31. We will spend the day with Grandfather. Why does Grandfather begin with a capital letter?
    a. Grandfather is the first word of the sentence.
    b. Grandfather is a special place to visit.
    c. Grandfather is at the end of the sentence.
    d. Grandfather is used as a name.

32. I brought papers books, and pencils to school. Where should another comma be placed in the sentence?
    a. before brought
    b. before papers
    c. before books
    d. before to

33. Wanda traveled _____ the country last week.
    a. too
    b. two
    c. to
    d. tow

34. Which of these is a correct sentence?
    a. laughed loudly movie
    b. She laughed loudly at the movie.
    c. On Wednesday, movie
    d. Where is the movie.

35. Abe said, Bring me my basketball. Which punctuation is needed in the sentence?
    a. question marks
    b. periods
    c. commas
    d. quotation marks

H. ➤ Editing: Read and choose the correct answer. *(10 points: 2 points each)*

"Ramona's Quiz"

(1) On Monday, ramona studied for three hours for her math quiz. (2) Her wanted to get a good grade. (3) On Tuesday, she studied fore four hours. (4) She was confident that she would do well on the quiz. (5) The teacher return the graded quizzes on Thursday. (6) She turned her paper over and saw that she had received an A. (7) Ramona was happy. (8) She was also proud of herself for doing sew well on the test.

---

36. In sentence 1, ramona is best written _____.
    a. Ramona
    b. "ramona"
    c. RAMONA
    d. as it is written

37. What change should you make to sentence 2?
    a. change *Her* to *She*
    b. change *to get* to *getting*
    c. change the period to a question mark
    d. make no change

38. What change should you make to sentence 3?
    a. change *On* to *At*
    b. change *Tuesday* to *Tusday*
    c. change *fore* to *for*
    d. make no change

39. What change should you make to sentence 4?
    a. change *She* to *Her*
    b. change *would* to *wood*
    c. change *on* to *for*
    d. make no change

TEST • Unit 2 (continued)

40. What change should you make to sentence 8?
  a. change *She* to *Her*
  b. change *herself* to *her*
  c. change *sew* to *so*
  d. make no change

I. ➤ Writing (20 points)

> **Writing Prompt** Write a fable explaining why a tiger roars. Use the Planning Guide to help you write.

Planning Guide
❑ Think of a reason why a tiger roars.
❑ Write this reason into a fable.
❑ Use personification.
❑ Make sure that your fable has a beginning, a middle, and an end.

QUIZ Unit 3 • Chapter 1

A. ➤ Vocabulary: Choose the correct answer. *(24 points: 4 points each)*

1. A _____ is a type of government where citizens vote for their leaders and representatives.
   a. peace
   b. democracy
   c. right
   d. freedom

2. _____ is applying laws in a way that is fair.
   a. Court
   b. Justice
   c. Movement
   d. Democracy

3. A(n) _____ is the freedom to do something by law.
   a. right
   b. allowance
   c. peace
   d. march

4. Words that are spelled the same but have different meanings and pronunciations are called _____.
   a. synonyms
   b. phrases
   c. clauses
   d. homographs

5. He <u>dove</u> into the swimming pool. In this sentence, <u>dove</u> means _____.
   a. a type of white bird
   b. a person who works for peace
   c. jumped headfirst into water
   d. opened a door for somebody

6. The sad story caused a <u>tear</u> to roll down his face. In this sentence, <u>tear</u> means _____.
   a. to rip up
   b. a rip in clothing
   c. to pull apart
   d. salty liquid from the eye

B. ➤ Text Structure/Elements of Literature: Read and choose the correct answer. *(24 points: 4 points each)*

"Drumbeats"

With energy

1 As I walk down the street, I shuffle to the rhythmic beat.
I love the sound of that big bass drum.

2 As I sit and watch the clouds, inside my head the tempo pounds.
I love the sound of that big bass drum.

---

7. "Drumbeats" is _____.
   a. a myth
   b. historical nonfiction
   c. a biography
   d. song lyrics

8. How many verses does "Drumbeats" have?
   a. 0
   b. 1
   c. 2
   d. 3

9. _____ is saying the same thing more than once.
   a. Repetition
   b. Direction
   c. Intonation
   d. Completion

10. Which line is the refrain in "Drumbeats"?
    a. As I walk down the street, I shuffle to the rhythmic beat.
    b. As I sit and watch the clouds, inside my head the tempo pounds.
    c. With energy
    d. I love the sound of that big bass drum.

QUIZ Unit 3 • Chapter 1 (continued)

11. Which is the direction line in "Drumbeats"?
    a. As I walk down the street, I shuffle to the rhythmic beat.
    b. As I sit and watch the clouds, inside my head the tempo pounds.
    c. *With energy*
    d. I love the sound of that big bass drum.

12. Repetition in a song shows that the singer _____ about the song's message.
    a. feels strongly
    b. does not care
    c. knows little
    d. dislikes

C. ➤ Reading Strategies: Choose the correct answer. *(12 points: 4 points each)*

13. To _____ is to use what you know to make a guess.
    a. write a summary
    b. make an inference
    c. analyze cause and effect
    d. use sequence of events

14. Hugo practices the piano every day. You can infer that _____.
    a. the piano is a loud instrument
    b. Hugo enjoys seeing plays
    c. Hugo likes playing the piano
    d. all of Hugo's friends play the piano

15. Keena left the party early. You can infer that _____.
    a. Keena was not having fun
    b. the party was at Jessica's house
    c. Keena works in a shoe store
    d. there were only a few people at the party

D. ➤ Grammar/Usage: Choose the correct answer. *(20 points: 4 points each)*

16. The future tense describes events that _____.
    a. already happened
    b. are happening now
    c. will never happen
    d. are going to happen

17. Which word shows future tense?
    a. does
    b. had
    c. will
    d. they

18. I think that people _____ on the moon 100 years from now.
    a. live
    b. will live
    c. did live
    d. have lived

19. Tomorrow, Alvaro and Ned _____ to my house.
    a. will come
    b. came
    c. did come
    d. have come

20. Which sentence shows future tense?
    a. Diego likes riding horses.
    b. Hiromi is my best friend.
    c. Hanna will call you next week.
    d. Michele worked in the yard all day.

E. ➤ Writing *(20 points)*

Writing Prompt Think about one way people can help each other. Write lyrics for a song about the way they can help. Use repetition, and give your song a title.

QUIZ Unit 3 • Chapter 2

A. ➤ Vocabulary: Choose the correct answer. *(28 points: 4 points each)*

1. Words with opposite meanings are _____.
   a. synonyms
   b. verbs
   c. prefixes
   d. antonyms

2. Abril washed the dirty dishes. An antonym for dirty is _____.
   a. filthy
   b. clean
   c. wet
   d. dry

3. A thesaurus is a book that lists _____.
   a. synonyms and antonyms
   b. nouns and verbs
   c. adjectives and adverbs
   d. subjects and pronouns

> **delete,** *v.* erase, cancel, take out, cross out; *ant.* add

4. In the thesaurus entry, what word is listed as the antonym of delete?
   a. cancel
   b. take out
   c. add
   d. erase

5. A contraction is _____.
   a. the beginning of a sentence
   b. two words put together to form a shorter word
   c. a sentence with more than one verb
   d. a group of words with similar meanings

6. What is the contraction for they and are?
   a. he's
   b. doesn't
   c. I'm
   d. they're

7. The contraction it's is made up of the words _____.
   a. she and is
   b. can and not
   c. it and is
   d. you and are

B. ➤ Text Structure/Elements of Literature: Read and choose the correct answer. *(24 points: 4 points each)*

> "Norma's Thoughts"
>
> 1   *December 13, 2002*
> 2   Dear Greta,
> 3   Today was my birthday! Mama, Diego, and I went to the beach. We went swimming and I found a conch shell! Later, we had pizza and cake at my favorite restaurant. Mama and Diego gave me roller blades. They were just what I wanted! Tomorrow, we're having a party in class. I'll tell you all about it. Good night!
> 4   Norma

8. In diaries, people _____.
   a. write important events and thoughts of each day
   b. list items that they need to buy at the store
   c. write stories that explain an event in nature
   d. list the main idea and details of a text

9. Who is the speaker in "Norma's Thoughts"?
   a. Greta
   b. Mama
   c. Norma
   d. Diego

10. What is the name of the diary in "Norma's Thoughts"?
    a. Norma
    b. Greta
    c. Diego
    d. Mama

QUIZ Unit 3 • Chapter 2 (continued)

11. _____ is how a writer thinks and feels about a subject or character.
    a. Meaning
    b. Conflict
    c. Tone
    d. Motivation

12. What is the tone of "Norma's Thoughts"?
    a. sad
    b. excited
    c. angry
    d. confused

13. On what date is Norma's class party?
    a. December 13
    b. December 14
    c. December 15
    d. December 16

C. ➤ Reading Strategies: Choose the correct answer. (16 points: 4 points each)

14. The sequence of events is _____.
    a. the order in which events happen
    b. the most important event in a text
    c. details that support the main idea
    d. a guess about what will happen next in a text

15. Amir rode his bike to the park and played baseball with his friends. Then he went home for lunch. At night, Amir went to the movies with Joe. The first thing that Amir did was _____.
    a. play baseball
    b. eat lunch
    c. go to the movies
    d. go to the park

16. After Amir ate lunch, he _____.
    a. rode his bike to the park
    b. went to the movies
    c. played baseball
    d. went home

17. What was the third thing that Amir did?
    a. went home for lunch
    b. went to the movies
    c. played baseball
    d. went to the park

D. ➤ Grammar/Usage: Choose the correct answer. (12 points: 4 points each)

18. Maria wants to take the exam. What is the infinitive in this sentence?
    a. Maria
    b. wants to
    c. to take
    d. the exam

19. You are ready to go home. What is the infinitive in this sentence?
    a. go home
    b. ready to
    c. You are
    d. to go

20. Sarit likes _____ there. Complete this sentence with an infinitive.
    a. it
    b. to be
    c. living
    d. is moving

E. ➤ Writing (20 points)

Writing Prompt Choose a problem that you had recently. Write a diary entry that explains the problem and how you solved it. Include the date and give the diary a name.

QUIZ Unit 3 • Chapter 3

A. ➤ Vocabulary: Choose the correct answer. *(24 points: 4 points each)*

1. Homophones are words that _____.
   a. sound the same but have different spellings and meanings
   b. have the same meaning but sound different
   c. describe actions
   d. describe the way something looks

2. A homophone for <u>pear</u> is _____.
   a. bear
   b. pare
   c. apple
   d. coin

3. We were mad that we had to <u>wait</u> for three hours. In this sentence, <u>wait</u> means _____.
   a. do something very important
   b. how heavy something is
   c. a type of song that people sing
   d. remain until something expected happens

4. A _____ is a body of water that moves in one direction.
   a. forest
   b. peach
   c. river
   d. mountain

5. _____ are tall forms of land and rock higher than hills.
   a. Pine trees
   b. Mountains
   c. Streams
   d. Deserts

6. A(n) _____ is a round, juicy fruit with a large seed inside it.
   a. peach
   b. banana
   c. pheasant
   d. ogre

B. ➤ Text Structure/Elements of Literature: Read and choose the correct answer. *(16 points: 4 points each)*

“Carlita the Brave”

1   Once upon a time, an evil king was stealing children. Carlita decided to stop the king. She walked to the forest even though her parents told her never to go there. The king's men grabbed her and took her to the castle with the other children. Carlita told the children to follow her. She brought them to a passage that led them out of the castle. Then Carlita clapped her hands and the castle fell to the ground.

---

7. “Carlita the Brave” is a _____.
   a. play
   b. poem
   c. speech
   d. folktale

8. What is the problem in “Carlita the Brave”?
   a. Carlita wants to be king.
   b. The king is stealing children.
   c. The castle falls over.
   d. Carlita walks to the forest.

9. What is the resolution in “Carlita the Brave”?
   a. Carlita is brave.
   b. The children do not listen to their parents.
   c. Carlita frees the children.
   d. The king's men take Carlita.

10. A folktale is _____.
    a. a story that is told from generation to generation
    b. a text that gives information about a topic
    c. the story of a person's life
    d. a text that gives directions on how to do something

QUIZ Unit 3 • Chapter 3 (continued)

C. ➤ Reading Strategies: Choose the correct answer. *(20 points: 4 points each)*

11. An effect is _____.
    a. the main character in a story
    b. a word that describes
    c. a picture that you form in your mind
    d. an event that happens as a result of a cause

12. A _____ is the reason an event happens.
    a. cause
    b. summary
    c. fact
    d. conclusion

13. The floor is covered with water. Which is the most likely cause?
    a. The dog ran away.
    b. Mai spilled a glass of water.
    c. Aaron bought a mop.
    d. Ida moved to New York.

14. My alarm clock did not go off. Which is the most likely effect?
    a. I ate lunch with Grandfather.
    b. My clothes got dirty.
    c. I was late for school.
    d. My mother bought a new car.

15. There was a strong wind. The light brown, wooden door slammed shut. What is the effect of the strong wind?
    a. The door is made of wood.
    b. The door is light brown.
    c. The door is open.
    d. The door slammed shut.

D. ➤ Grammar/Usage: Choose the correct answer. *(20 points: 4 points each)*

16. A conjunction is a _____.
    a. word that describes an action
    b. word that describes a noun
    c. word that joins parts of a sentence
    d. sentence part that tells when something happened

17. Which word can be used as a conjunction?
    a. and
    b. he
    c. their
    d. you

18. A(n) _____ is two complete sentences joined by a conjunction.
    a. compound sentence
    b. simple sentence
    c. complex sentence
    d. incomplete sentence

19. Which is a compound sentence?
    a. Lionel is the best piano player that I know.
    b. Adam wants pizza, and Laura wants salad.
    c. Yumi and I are best friends.
    d. Tell her that you cannot see the board.

20. Elena wanted the book. Her friend gave it to her. The compound sentence is:
    a. Elena and her friend both wanted the book.
    b. Her friend gave Elena the book.
    c. Elena told her friend that she wanted the book.
    d. Elena wanted the book, and her friend gave it to her.

E. ➤ Writing *(20 points)*

> **Writing Prompt** Choose a book that you have read recently. Write a summary. Make sure to write about the main character and the problem he or she solved.

QUIZ Unit 3 • Chapter 4

A. ➤ **Vocabulary:** Choose the correct answer. *(28 points: 4 points each)*

1. _____ are two words with similar meanings.
   a. Adjectives
   b. Synonyms
   c. Conjunctions
   d. Prefixes

2. I planted the tree in the <u>earth</u>. A synonym for <u>earth</u> is _____.
   a. water
   b. moon
   c. sun
   d. dirt

3. We ate cake at the <u>celebration</u>. A synonym for <u>celebration</u> is _____.
   a. party
   b. school
   c. store
   d. newspaper

4. A _____ is a group of letters added to the beginning of a word.
   a. suffix
   b. pronoun
   c. verb
   d. prefix

5. Which word has a prefix?
   a. band
   b. sadly
   c. doctor
   d. disagree

6. To _____ is to put an end to something.
   a. recontinue
   b. discontinue
   c. continue
   d. continuity

7. A _____ person does not tell the truth.
   a. dishonest
   b. dismissed
   c. distinct
   d. discouraged

B. ➤ **Text Structure/Elements of Literature:** Read and choose the correct answer. *(28 points: 4 points each)*

"A Big Mistake"

1 Finally, it was the day of the big race. I stretched my legs and took my position at the starting line. I could hear my parents cheering for me. I took a deep breath and waited. "GO!" shouted the announcer, and I sprinted off. Before I made it around the first turn, I tripped! I had forgotten to tie my shoelaces! My dreams of winning were over.

---

8. "A Big Mistake" is a _____.
   a. nonfiction article
   b. fable
   c. personal narrative
   d. biography

9. What is the problem in "A Big Mistake"?
   a. The author forgets her shoes.
   b. The author wakes up late for the race.
   c. There are only a few people in the race.
   d. The author forgets to tie her shoelaces.

10. A personal narrative _____.
    a. uses first-person point of view
    b. uses third-person point of view
    c. includes made-up experiences
    d. is not about the author

11. _____ are how characters look and act.
    a. Moods
    b. Inferences
    c. Settings
    d. Traits

12. The reason why characters do things is _____.
    a. sequence
    b. motivation
    c. point of view
    d. resolution

QUIZ Unit 3 • Chapter 4 (continued)

13. In "A Big Mistake," one of the author's traits is that she is _____.
    a. tall
    b. smart
    c. forgetful
    d. mean

14. Opinions and beliefs are a character's _____.
    a. plot
    b. style
    c. text evidence
    d. point of view

C. ➤ Reading Strategies: Choose the correct answer. (12 points: 4 points each)

15. To summarize is to _____.
    a. show how two things are similar
    b. find a definition in a dictionary
    c. write the most important ideas of a text
    d. describe why an event happened

16. I wish I lived in California. It has beaches and mountains. The weather is warm most of the year. It also has many nice cities. Which sentence summarizes this paragraph?
    a. California's weather is usually warm.
    b. California is a great place to live.
    c. California has many different places to visit.
    d. Many of California's cities are lovely.

17. Bo needs extra help with math. He stays after school to ask his teacher questions. He also does math problems with his father. Which sentence summarizes this paragraph?
    a. Bo dislikes math.
    b. Bo's teacher answers Bo's questions.
    c. Bo's father helps Bo with math.
    d. Bo works hard to improve his math skills.

D. ➤ Grammar/Usage: Choose the correct answer. (12 points: 4 points each)

18. The word could describes _____.
    a. what you were able to do in the past
    b. what you may do in the future
    c. what you are doing right now
    d. how you feel right now

19. If you were unable to finish something, then you _____ finish it.
    a. could
    b. couldn't
    c. will
    d. should

20. The word couldn't is made of the words _____.
    a. will/not
    b. should/not
    c. can/not
    d. could/not

E. ➤ Writing (20 points)

> **Writing Prompt** Finish this paragraph. Make sure to explain your choice.
>
> *I knew I had made a mistake. I knew that I had to call. I decided . . .*

QUIZ Unit 3 • Chapter 5

A. ➤ Vocabulary: Choose the correct answer. *(28 points: 4 points each)*

> **physician** /fɪˈzɪʃən/ *n.* a person who is qualified to practice medicine; a doctor of medicine: *A physician cures sick people.* [Greek *physikē'* "science of nature"]

1. What is the first sound in *physician*?
   a. /z/
   b. /p/
   c. /f/
   d. /n/

2. The word *physician* comes from _____.
   a. Greek
   b. Latin
   c. Old English
   d. French

3. A physician is _____.
   a. the science of nature
   b. a verb
   c. a doctor
   d. a type of medicine

4. Climbing a mountain is a _____.
   a. distress
   b. challenge
   c. physical
   d. correction

5. Swimming is a _____ activity.
   a. mental
   b. tension
   c. stress
   d. physical

6. Which is a mental activity?
   a. bicycling
   b. ice skating
   c. eating
   d. thinking

7. Which of these is likely to cause tension?
   a. a funny joke
   b. an interesting book
   c. a difficult test
   d. a happy song

B. ➤ Text Structure/Elements of Literature: Read and choose the correct answer. *(16 points: 4 points each)*

> "Guitar Lessons"
>
> 1 **Finding Your Perfect Instrument**
> 2 Buying a guitar is exciting. But it may also be confusing. Before you buy a guitar, make sure you do some research to decide which one is right for you. Take notes on the different types of guitars. How do they sound? Are they comfortable in your hands? Remember: Just like people, each guitar is unique. Your friend's guitar may not necessarily be the perfect instrument for you.

8. An informational text _____.
   a. gives information about a topic
   b. lists synonyms and antonyms
   c. describes an author's feelings about a subject
   d. is usually spoken aloud and written down later

9. "Guitar Lessons" gives information about _____.
   a. the history of guitars
   b. the author's favorite guitar
   c. finding the right guitar
   d. how to play the guitar

10. The heading in the reading is _____.
    a. "Guitar Lessons"
    b. Finding Your Perfect Instrument
    c. the first sentence
    d. the last sentence

QUIZ Unit 3 • Chapter 5 (continued)

11. You want to learn how to clean a guitar. Which heading would you look under?
    a. Guitar Making: A History
    b. Making Music on a Guitar
    c. Performing for Friends and Family
    d. Caring for Your Guitar

C. ➤ **Reading Strategies:** Choose the correct answer. *(16 points: 4 points each)*

12. The main idea is _____.
    a. the most important idea in a text
    b. a statement that can be proven true
    c. what characters say in a text
    d. how two things are different

13. _____ supports a main idea.
    a. An opinion
    b. Chronology
    c. A root word
    d. A detail

14. "I do not feel very well," said Eduardo. "My stomach hurts. I think I ate too many cookies." What is the main idea of this paragraph?
    a. Eduardo ate cookies.
    b. Eduardo likes cookies.
    c. Eduardo feels sick.
    d. Eduardo should have eaten a sandwich.

15. In this paragraph, which detail supports this main idea?
    a. Eduardo's stomach hurts.
    b. Eduardo will eat fewer cookies next time.
    c. Eduardo likes to eat.
    d. Eduardo is 15 years old.

D. ➤ **Grammar/Usage:** Choose the correct answer. *(20 points: 4 points each)*

16. A(n) _____ can stand on its own as a sentence.
    a. independent clause
    b. dependent clause
    c. conditional sentence
    d. complex sentence

17. Which is a conditional sentence?
    a. If you practice, you will improve.
    b. Aaron is a very nice person.
    c. I like dancing, and Rana likes singing.
    d. We had fun at the party yesterday.

18. If it rains, we will go to the movies. What is the independent clause?
    a. we will go
    b. we will go to the movies
    c. if it rains
    d. to the movies

19. If the music is good, I like to dance. What is the dependent clause?
    a. If the music
    b. If the music is good
    c. I like
    d. I like to dance

20. Choose the dependent clause to complete this sentence: _____, we will call you.
    a. We are going and
    b. Susie and I
    c. If we go
    d. Wait for us

E. ➤ **Writing** *(20 points)*

> **Writing Prompt** Choose an activity in which two people must work together. Write an informational text explaining the activity. Tell the reader how to begin the activity and all of the steps necessary to complete it.

TEST • Unit 3

A. ➤ Reading

The Right Way to Help

1   Once I got lost in the city. I got off of the subway at the wrong stop. I decided to ask a man for directions. I then noticed he was blind. "Oh, I'm sorry," I mumbled and started to go, but he stopped me. "It's OK," he said  and pointed to the right. He did know his way around, even if I didn't.

2   That man was very proud of how well he could get around. He didn't need me to feel sorry for him. I was the one who was lost! He couldn't see, but he had worked hard to do most things on his own. He had to meet many challenges and I will always admire that. I like people who dare to do things.

3   I learned a lot from that meeting. A few years later I was in college. One of my classmates, Wade, was blind. Wade taught me even more. He told me the right things to say when I was with a blind person. He also let me help him when he asked. So, I learned the right way to help blind people.

4   Suppose you see a blind person who needs help. This is what Wade told me to do. Touch the blind person's arm lightly and ask, "May I help you?" Chat with the person just as you would with anyone. Don't worry if you find yourself using words like "look," "see," or "watch." Whatever you do, don't shout!

TEST • Unit 3 (continued)

B. ➤ Reading Comprehension: Choose the correct answer. *(20 points: 2 points each)*

1. What mistake did the narrator make?
   a. he got off at the wrong subway stop
   b. he couldn't find his map
   c. he forgot the address
   d. he had wrong directions

2. What did the narrator ask the man in the city?
   a. He asked what time it was.
   b. He asked for directions.
   c. He asked why he was blind.
   d. He asked if he could help him.

3. The narrator admired the man who helped him because _____.
   a. he felt sorry for other people
   b. he had a job on the subway
   c. he had gone to college
   d. he worked hard to do things on his own

4. The narrator likes people who _____.
   a. admit they are lost
   b. dare to do things
   c. never get lost
   d. know the right things to say

5. Why did the narrator remember the man in the subway?
   a. He got lost again in the city.
   b. He wanted to find the man again.
   c. He learned a lot from the man.
   d. He felt sorry for the man.

6. How did the narrator know Wade?
   a. Wade was his friend at college.
   b. Wade was his brother.
   c. Wade was a worker at the subway.
   d. Wade was his teacher.

7. The narrator listened to Wade's views because he knew about _____.
   a. cities
   b. friendship
   c. blindness
   d. school

8. Wade taught the narrator about _____.
   a. finding your way in the city
   b. helping blind people
   c. taking the subway
   d. doing well in college

9. If you want to help a blind person, what is the first thing to do?
   a. Touch the person's arm lightly.
   b. Shout at the person.
   c. Wait for the person to speak.
   d. Be sure not to use certain words.

10. How do you know that Wade trusted the narrator?
    a. Wade let the narrator help him.
    b. Wade asked the narrator for directions.
    c. Wade dared the narrator to do things.
    d. Wade told the narrator not to worry.

TEST • Unit 3 (continued)

C. ➤ Reading Strategies: Choose the correct answer. *(10 points: 2 points each)*

11. From information in the story, you can infer that the narrator is a _____ person.
    a. selfish
    b. talkative
    c. kind
    d. busy

12. Which words from the story help you understand the order of events?
    a. "I got off the subway"
    b. "I decided to ask"
    c. "That man was very proud"
    d. "A few years later"

13. Why does the narrator say he is sorry to the blind man?
    a. He didn't know he was blind.
    b. He bumped into him by accident.
    c. He couldn't help the man find his way.
    d. He didn't know the right way to help him.

14. What is the best way to summarize paragraph 3?
    a. The narrator learned a lot in his college classes.
    b. The narrator learned about how blind people read.
    c. Wade and the narrator became best friends.
    d. Wade taught the narrator the right way to help blind people.

15. The picture of the street supports the idea that it is easy to get lost in the city because _____.
    a. it is so busy
    b. it is so small
    c. it is so empty
    d. it is so lonely

D. ➤ Elements of Literature: Choose the correct answer. *(10 points: 2 points each)*

16. The tone of the story is _____.
    a. admiring
    b. sad
    c. angry
    d. joyful

17. At the beginning of the story, what is the narrator's problem?
    a. He feels lonely for his friends.
    b. He doesn't know how to make friends.
    c. He can't find his way in the city.
    d. He hurts the blind man's feelings.

18. How does the narrator solve his problem?
    a. He asks for help from the blind man.
    b. He asks a police officer for directions.
    c. He calls a college friend for advice.
    d. He uses a compass to find his way.

19. You would find more information about the topic of this story under the heading _____.
    a. How to Make New Friends
    b. Common Reasons for Blindness
    c. Helping a Blind Person
    d. How Blind People Read

20. The story is told from the point of view of _____.
    a. a classmate
    b. the narrator
    c. a college teacher
    d. the blind man

TEST • Unit 3 (continued)

E. ➤ Vocabulary: Choose the correct answer. *(10 points: 2 points each)*

21. Which word is related to the words <u>justice</u> and <u>peace</u>?
  a. lost
  b. decided
  c. rights
  d. dare

22. The antonym of <u>mumbled</u> is _____.
  a. whispered
  b. hinted
  c. shouted
  d. murmured

23. Which sentence contains a contraction?
  a. "It's okay," he said and pointed to the right.
  b. "I learned a lot from that meeting."
  c. "One of my classmates was blind."
  d. "This is what Wade told me to do."

24. Which word is a homophone?
  a. worry
  b. using
  c. words
  d. see

---

college /ˈkɑlɪʤ/ *n.* in the USA, an institution of higher or professional education: *a four-year college, a community college* [Latin *collegium* society].

---

25. What language does the word *college* come from?
  a. French
  b. German
  c. English
  d. Latin

F. ➤ Grammar/Usage: Choose the correct answer. *(10 points: 2 points each)*

26. Tomorrow, I _____ my friends after school.
  a. will help
  b. helped
  c. helping
  d. had helped

27. I want to read an exciting novel in the library. The infinitive verb is _____.
  a. I want
  b. to read
  c. an exciting novel
  d. in the library

28. Which is a correct compound sentence?
  a. My sister got the seeds. I planted them.
  b. My sister got the seeds, and I planted them.
  c. After my sister got the seeds, I planted them.
  d. My sister got the seeds, I planted them.

29. The past tense of <u>can</u> is _____.
  a. can't
  b. cannot
  c. could
  d. cant

30. Which is a correct complex sentence?
  a. If you like computers, you should read this book.
  b. Leon plays the piano and he writes music, too.
  c. Mrs. Brown likes art, so do I.
  d. Carmen wrote the story and Tim drew the pictures.

TEST • Unit 3 (continued)

G. ➤ Writing Conventions (10 points: 2 points each)

31. My English teacher grew up in Detroit Michigan. A comma should be placed after _____.
    a. English
    b. up
    c. Detroit
    d. Michigan

32. In the greeting of a friendly letter, which is correct?
    a. Dear Juan and Lupe,
    b. Dear Juan and lupe,
    c. dear Juan and Lupe,
    d. dear Juan And Lupe,

33. Which sentence uses correct capitalization?
    a. Lucy's Grandfather took us fishing.
    b. I visit Aunt Maya every summer.
    c. My Cousin, Felipe, is a good swimmer.
    d. We played soccer with aunt Ana.

34. What change should you make to this sentence: Here are the things I need from my school locker a notebook, pen, and paper.
    a. place a comma after things
    b. change the s to S in school
    c. place a colon after locker
    d. remove the comma after notebook

35. What change should you make to this sentence: "Martin do you have a notebook and a pencil?" asked the art teacher.
    a. add a comma after Martin
    b. change the question mark to a period
    c. add a comma after notebook
    d. change art to Art

H. ➤ Editing: Read and choose the correct answer. (10 points: 2 points each)

"A Special Place"

(1) Almost every day, I visit a special place after school. (2) It is a friendly, busy place where I can always find something new to do. (3) Sometimes my friends and I go to do their homework. (4) Other times I use the computers to find information or play games. (5) Every week I take out a new book. (6) My Cousin, José, finds an interesting book, too. (7) We try to finish our books by Friday. (8) José finished his last book on Friday May 1. (9) Next week, I finish my book first.

(10) Then I will look through the library for another great book or magazine to read!

36. In sentence 2, what is the contraction for It is?
    a. Its
    b. Its'
    c. It's
    d. I'ts

37. What change should you make to sentence 3?
    a. change *my* to *mine*
    b. change *to do* to *doing*
    c. change *their* to *our*
    d. make no change

38. What change should you make to sentence 6?
    a. change *My* to *my*
    b. change *Cousin* to *cousin*
    c. change *José* to *josé*
    d. make no change

TEST • Unit 3 *(continued)*

39. What change should you make to sentence 8?

   a. change *José* to *josé*

   b. change *finished* to *finishes*

   c. add a comma after *Friday*

   d. make no change

40. What change should you make to sentence 9?

   a. change *finish* to *will finish*

   b. change *finish* to *finishes*

   c. add a comma after *finish*

   d. change *my* to *my's*

I. ➤ **Writing** *(20 points)*

Choose a topic that you are interested in and know a lot about. Write an informational text like *The Right Way to Help*. Include details that support your main idea. Use the Planning Guide to help you write.

Planning Guide

❑ Brainstorm topics that you know a lot about.

❑ Choose one topic.

❑ Write down ideas and details about the topic.

❑ Use these details and ideas to write your informational text.

❑ Check your writing for correct spelling, capitalization, and punctuation.

MID-BOOK EXAM

A. ➤ Reading

What's the Difference?

1   What is that animal you just saw hop in front of you? Is it a toad or a frog? It's easy to get these two amphibians mixed up. Maybe some of the following information will help you tell the two apart.

2   Both the frog and the toad live on land and in the water. Both hatch from eggs laid in the water. However, frogs spend more time in the water than toads.

3   There are many different kinds of frogs, but some traits are true of all frogs. One is that frogs have smooth, wet skin. They also have strong back legs for hopping, and their camouflage skin matches their environment.

4   Toads, on the other hand, do not have smooth skin and their skin is dry. Also, their back legs are not as powerful as a frog's.

    By the way, that was a tree toad that just hopped in front of you.

From Kim's Diary

1 Friday, September 21

2   Mr. Ramos asked us to look for animals that live around Hill's pond. We have to take notes, and then write about what we saw.

3   I don't know if I will see anything! After all, we just learned about animal camouflage. How will I even see them?

4   Well, I guess I know what I will be doing tomorrow. I will be waiting and watching.

5 Saturday, September 22

6   I saw something! First, I heard a splash, but I could not see anything. Then, out of the water pops this frog! It got up on a big rock and just sat there. At least that is what I thought. Out came its tongue, and then there was one less fly in the world. It happened so quickly!

MID-BOOK EXAM (continued)

B. ➤ Reading Comprehension: Read and choose the correct answer.
(20 points: 2 points each)

Example: Toads and frogs are both _____.
a. insects
b. lizards
(c.) amphibians
d. land animals

1. "What's the Difference?" is a(n) _____.
a. informational text
b. biography
c. folktale
d. personal narrative

2. How are frogs and toads different?
a. A toad lives on land, while a frog lives in water.
b. A toad has stronger legs than a frog.
c. A frog spends more time in water than a toad.
d. A frog hatches from an egg, but a toad does not.

3. How are frogs and toads similar?
a. They both have smooth skin.
b. They both have strong back legs.
c. They are both amphibians.
d. They are both colorful.

4. Based on what you read in "From Kim's Diary" you can infer that frogs _____.
a. make great pets
b. eat flies
c. lay many eggs
d. are bigger than toads

5. Kim looks for animals near a(n) _____.
a. pond
b. river
c. ocean
d. lake

6. In "From Kim's Diary," Mr. Ramos is most likely _____.
a. Kim's father
b. Kim's teacher
c. Kim's brother
d. Kim's friend

7. In "From Kim's Diary," what happened right after the frog got up on the rock?
a. Kim heard a splash.
b. Kim watched as the frog ate a fly.
c. Kim saw the frog's tongue.
d. Kim got scared and left.

8. "From Kim's Diary" is organized by _____.
a. comparing and contrasting information
b. putting events in the order they occurred
c. explaining cause and effect relationships
d. putting events in the order of importance

9. Both readings _____.
a. are diary entries
b. are about frogs
c. are about school
d. have the same author

10. Which of the following sentences is an opinion?
a. There are many kinds of frogs.
b. Frogs spend time in the water.
c. Kim is a nice person.
d. Kim saw a frog jump out of the water.

MID-BOOK EXAM (continued)

C. ➤ **Reading Strategies:** Read and choose the correct answer. *(10 points: 2 points each)*

11. What is the main idea of "What's the Difference?"
    a. Frogs and toads have similarities and differences.
    b. People get frogs and toads mixed up all the time.
    c. There are many kinds of frogs and toads.
    d. Frogs and toads enjoy hopping during the day.

12. Summarize paragraph 3 in "What's the Difference?"
    a. There are many different kinds of frogs.
    b. Frogs like to spend time hopping.
    c. Frogs have smooth, wet skin, and strong back legs.
    d. Frogs and toads are very different.

13. Frogs and toads both _____.
    a. live on land and water
    b. hatch eggs on land
    c. have smooth skin
    d. have dry skin

14. In "From Kim's Diary," why do you think Mr. Ramos wants Kim to take notes on what she saw?
    a. to remember what she observed
    b. to practice cursive writing
    c. to write a book about her findings
    d. to make sure she looked for animals

15. In "From Kim's Diary," why did the frog sit on the rock?
    a. He was feeding his babies.
    b. He wanted to dry off.
    c. He wanted to eat.
    d. He was afraid of being eaten.

D. ➤ **Elements of Literature:** Choose the correct answer. *(10 points: 2 points each)*

16. Why did the author write "From Kim's Diary"?
    a. to give the reader information
    b. to entertain the reader
    c. to express an opinion
    d. to persuade the reader

17. "From Kim's Diary" is told from a _____.
    a. first-person point of view
    b. second-person point of view
    c. third-person point of view
    d. dramatic-point of view

18. In "From Kim's Diary," what is the tone of paragraph 6?
    a. excited
    b. angry
    c. joking
    d. worried

19. What motivated Kim to look for animals?
    a. She had a love for animals.
    b. Mr. Ramos asked her to do it.
    c. Her mother suggested it to her.
    d. Her friend wanted her to do it.

20. Which two words from the readings rhyme?
    a. up and us
    b. wet and well
    c. dry and fly
    d. most and just

MID-BOOK EXAM (continued)

E. ➤ **Vocabulary:** Choose the correct answer. *(10 points: 2 points each)*

21. Which word from "From Kim's Diary" is a compound word?
  a. tomorrow
  b. something
  c. camouflage
  d. that's

22. From the context of paragraph 3 in "What's the Difference?" you know that the word camouflage means _____.
  a. designed to hide
  b. brightly colored
  c. good for jumping
  d. a different kind

23. Their back legs are not as powerful as a frog's. The word powerful means _____.
  a. having power
  b. without power
  c. remove power
  d. giving power

24. The words live /lɪv/ and live /laɪv/ are _____.
  a. synonyms
  b. antonyms
  c. homographs
  d. contractions

25. In paragraph 3 of "From Kim's Diary," the contraction don't is made up of the words _____.
  a. doing not
  b. did not
  c. does not
  d. do not

F. ➤ **Grammar/Usage:** Choose the correct answer. *(10 points: 2 points each)*

26. Which sentence contains a comparative adjective?
  a. Susan is the shortest person on the team.
  b. The apple juice is too sweet!
  c. It is colder today than it was yesterday.
  d. He studied hard for the math test.

27. Which of the underlined words in the sentences is the subject?
  a. Ernesto wrote a beautiful poem for his mother.
  b. Ernesto wrote a beautiful poem for his mother.
  c. Ernesto wrote a beautiful poem for his mother.
  d. Ernesto wrote a beautiful poem for his mother.

28. Which sentence is written in the future tense?
  a. Maria walks her dog.
  b. Maria walked her dog.
  c. Maria will walk her dog.
  d. Maria is walking her dog.

29. Which sentence from the readings contains a subject pronoun?
  a. We have to take notes, and then write what we saw.
  b. Then, out of the water pops this frog!
  c. One is that frogs have smooth, wet skin.
  d. At least that is what I thought.

30. Tanya wants to cook dinner for her family and friends. This sentence _____.
  a. is in the past tense
  b. is in the future tense
  c. contains a contraction
  d. contains an infinitive

MID-BOOK EXAM (continued)

G. ➤ Writing Conventions: Choose the correct answer. *(10 points: 2 points each)*

31. I need _____ loaves of bread.
  a. tow
  b. too
  c. two
  d. to

32. Which word has the long *i* sound?
  a. friend
  b. their
  c. dime
  d. little

33. Which sentence uses correct capitalization?
  a. I made grandpa Joe a special card.
  b. We ate turkey and stuffing on thanksgiving.
  c. I live in the united states of america.
  d. Juan told Dr. Smith he had a sore throat.

34. Which sentence uses correct punctuation?
  a. Armondo was born on March, 16 1980.
  b. Marcela lives in St. Louis, Missouri.
  c. Jose wo'nt go to bed past 9:00.
  d. Stacys' cousin is visiting next week.

35. Which sentence uses correct punctuation?
  a. What time does the library close.
  b. The library has books computers and other resources.
  c. The new library will open on August 5, 2007.
  d. Reference, aids can help you find information.

H. ➤ Editing: Choose the correct answer. *(10 points: 2 points each)*

"Saturday Dinner"

(1) They like to try different places to eat. (2) Last week, we could not decide where we wanted to eat. (3) After we voted, my family decided we will go to our favorite pizza place. (4) Doesn't this seem like a fun way to spend a Saturday evening. (5) Every Saturday, my family goes out to dinner.

36. In sentence 1, They is best written _____.
  a. Us
  b. We
  c. She
  d. Them

37. In sentence 2, the words could not can be written as the contraction _____.
  a. couldn't
  b. can't
  c. cannot
  d. wouldn't

38. What change should you make to sentence 3?
  a. change *decided* to *decide*
  b. change *will go* to *would go*
  c. change *our* to *us*
  d. make no change

39. What change should you make to sentence 4?
  a. change *Doesn't* to *Do not*
  b. change *to spend* to *spending*
  c. change the period to a question mark
  d. make no change

MID-BOOK EXAM (continued)

40. What change should you make to the organization of the paragraph?
   a. move sentence 5 to the beginning of the paragraph
   b. move sentence 5 after sentence 2
   c. move sentence 5 after sentence 3
   d. make no change

I. ➤ Writing (20 points)

> **Writing Prompt** Write three paragraphs about a special tradition you celebrate. Use the Planning Guide to help you write.

Planning Guide
❑ In paragraph 1, tell what your tradition is and why you celebrate it.
❑ In paragraph 2, give details about your tradition and explain how you celebrate it.
❑ In paragraph 3, tell why this tradition is important to you.
❑ Use first-person point of view.
❑ Check your writing for correct spelling, capitalization, and punctuation.

QUIZ Unit 4 • Chapter 1

A. ➤ Vocabulary: Choose the correct answer. *(20 points: 4 points each)*

1. A(n) _____ is a group of letters added to the end of a word.
   a. prefix
   b. antonym
   c. thesaurus
   d. suffix

2. The word _____ means "in a pleasant manner."
   a. pleasantly
   b. unpleasant
   c. pleasantish
   d. pleasantness

3. The soft wind blew _____ through the trees.
   a. roughly
   b. loudly
   c. quietly
   d. quickly

4. You can learn the meanings of new words by _____.
   a. making inferences
   b. finding meanings in a text
   c. finding the main idea
   d. understanding sequence of events

5. A(n) _____ describes why, how, or where something happened.
   a. adverb
   b. homonym
   c. noun
   d. suffix

B. ➤ Text Structure/Elements of Literature: Read and choose the correct answer. *(24 points: 4 points each)*

> "The Man and the Apple Tree"
>
> 1   One day, a greedy man found an apple tree. The man picked all the apples and didn't leave any for others to enjoy. The next day the man went back to the tree, but it was gone. Johnny Appleseed, guardian of the forest, was standing in its place. "Where is *my* tree?!" demanded the man. Johnny Appleseed replied, "When you learn to share, the apple tree will return."

6. "The Man and the Apple Tree" is an example of _____.
   a. science fiction
   b. nonfiction
   c. a legend
   d. a biography

7. What does "The Man and the Apple Tree" teach?
   a. People should not be greedy.
   b. Apples are delicious.
   c. People should not cut down trees.
   d. People should share only some things.

8. In a legend, the main character is often a(n) _____.
   a. apple
   b. tree
   c. child
   d. hero

9. Legends often use _____ to make heroes seem greater than they really are.
   a. chronology
   b. exaggeration
   c. dialogue
   d. contractions

QUIZ Unit 4 • Chapter 1 (continued)

10. A _____ is a less important character in a story.
    a. main character
    b. fictional character
    c. minor character
    d. human character

11. The _____ is the most important character in a story.
    a. main character
    b. mythical character
    c. minor character
    d. human character

C. ➤ Reading Strategies: Choose the correct answer. *(12 points: 4 points each)*

12. When you make a prediction, you _____.
    a. determine the most important idea in a text
    b. use text clues to guess what might happen next
    c. analyze the reasons why an event happens
    d. take notes on the setting

13. Monique puts on her shoes and coat. You can predict that she will _____.
    a. walk outside
    b. take a shower
    c. go to sleep
    d. go swimming

14. Koji misses his friend. You can predict that he will _____.
    a. ask his sister to clean his room
    b. get an A on a test
    c. play a video game
    d. write a letter to his friend

D. ➤ Grammar/Usage: Choose the correct answer. *(24 points: 4 points each)*

15. Which word is a preposition?
    a. you   c. in
    b. car   d. the

16. A _____ is a group of words that starts with a preposition and contains a noun or pronoun as its object.
    a. prepositional phrase
    b. simple sentence
    c. reference source
    d. compound word

17. Which is a prepositional phrase?
    a. Pablo is here
    b. under the table
    c. the village
    d. her cat, Sandy

18. The book is on my desk. The object of the preposition is _____.
    a. book
    b. on
    c. is
    d. desk

19. Irma is standing on the sidewalk. The preposition is _____.
    a. I
    b. on
    c. sidewalk
    d. is

20. Which sentence contains a prepositional phrase?
    a. When Chuck is ready, we will leave.
    b. The chair was made last year.
    c. The lady is at the store.
    d. The door suddenly slammed.

E. ➤ Writing *(20 points)*

Writing Prompt Think of a present-day hero. Write a legend describing something great that this hero does.

QUIZ Unit 4 • Chapter 2

A. ➤ Vocabulary: Choose the correct answer. *(24 points: 4 points each)*

1. A prefix is a group of letters that _____.
   a. is added to the end of a word
   b. describes an action
   c. is added to the beginning of a word
   d. is added to the middle of a word

2. The prefix *un-* means _____.
   a. in a certain manner
   b. not
   c. with
   d. before

3. The little boy cried because he was _____.
   a. unhappy
   b. unbelievable
   c. unintelligent
   d. unhelpful

4. The word _____ means "not done, not complete."
   a. unequal
   b. unfair
   c. ungrateful
   d. unfinished

5. The _____ is a baseball contest.
   a. World Series
   b. Super Bowl
   c. National Football League
   d. National Hockey League

6. _____ is the professional baseball league in the United States.
   a. The World Series
   b. Gold Glove
   c. Major League Baseball
   d. The Super Bowl

B. ➤ Text Structure/Elements of Literature: Read and choose the correct answer. *(20 points: 4 points each)*

"Ma Ferguson"

1   Miriam "Ma" Ferguson was the first female governor of Texas. She was born in Texas in 1875. In 1914 Ferguson served as First Lady of Texas when her husband became governor. Ten years later, Ferguson herself was elected governor and served two terms. She remained involved in politics until her death in 1961.

---

7. "Ma Ferguson" is a(n) _____.
   a. autobiography
   b. personal narrative
   c. persuasive speech
   d. biography

8. In "Ma Ferguson," what important event happened in 1924?
   a. Ferguson became First Lady of Texas.
   b. Ferguson was born in Texas.
   c. Ferguson became governor of Texas.
   d. Ferguson finished college.

9. "Ma Ferguson" uses _____ point of view.
   a. third-person
   b. second-person
   c. first-person
   d. no

10. Which sentence is written in third-person point of view?
    a. I enjoy mystery novels.
    b. You are a terrific artist!
    c. He was born in Mexico.
    d. We cannot go with you.

11. In a biography, the author _____.
    a. describes made-up events
    b. tells the story of another person's life
    c. explains steps in a process
    d. tells the story of his or her own life

QUIZ Unit 4 • Chapter 2 (continued)

C. ➤ **Reading Strategies:** Choose the correct answer. *(20 points: 4 points each)*

12. Chronological order is _____.
   a. the order in which events happen
   b. pictures that you form in your mind
   c. the reason why an event happens
   d. language that compares one thing to another

13. This morning, Eze ate breakfast. Then she met her friend Juan at the art museum. After that, she went home. Then she read her book until it was time for bed. What did Eze do after she went home?
   a. She ate breakfast.
   b. She went to the art museum.
   c. She said goodbye to Juan.
   d. She read her book.

14. What did Eze do first?
   a. She ate breakfast.
   b. She met her friend Juan.
   c. She went home.
   d. She went to the art museum.

15. Mario wakes up in the morning. Then, he _____.
   a. goes to sleep at night
   b. eats dinner
   c. gets out of bed
   d. plays basketball after school

16. Rosa _____. Then, she hangs up the telephone.
   a. brings her groceries home
   b. speaks to her friend on the telephone
   c. went to the art museum
   d. began her homework

D. ➤ **Grammar/Usage:** Choose the correct answer. *(16 points: 4 points each)*

17. A _____ can tell you when something happened.
   a. definition
   b. suffix
   c. root word
   d. prepositional phrase

18. Which sentence is correct?
   a. I am working in Monday.
   b. The car was made on 1999.
   c. The test is on Wednesday.
   d. She is moving on October.

19. He was born _____ February 12, 1988.
   a. on
   b. at
   c. in
   d. by

20. My sister was born _____ 2002.
   a. for
   b. in
   c. on
   d. to

E. ➤ **Writing** *(20 points)*

> **Writing Prompt** Write your own biography as if another person wrote it. Use third-person point of view.

Grade

QUIZ Unit 4 • Chapter 3

A. ➤ Vocabulary: Choose the correct answer. *(24 points: 4 points each)*

1. Words that are pronounced and often spelled the same but have different meanings are called ____.
   a. contractions
   b. homonyms
   c. dialogue
   d. synonyms

2. I <u>like</u> candy. In this sentence, <u>like</u> means ____.
   a. something that is bad
   b. something that is similar
   c. to enjoy
   d. to think about

3. José looks <u>like</u> his father. In this sentence, <u>like</u> means ____.
   a. something that is bad
   b. something that is similar
   c. to enjoy
   d. to think about

4. What is the root word in <u>correction</u>?
   a. core
   b. ion
   c. correct
   d. rection

5. The suffix *-ion* changes ____.
   a. verbs into nouns
   b. synonyms into antonyms
   c. adverbs into pronouns
   d. adjectives into verbs

6. The fighting caused much <u>destruction</u>. In this sentence, <u>destruction</u> means ____.
   a. the act of building
   b. a state of happiness
   c. a state of nervousness
   d. the act of destroying

B. ➤ Text Structure/Elements of Literature: Read and choose the correct answer. *(28 points: 4 points each)*

> "Steven Spielberg: Movie Maker"
>
> 1 "Mom, I want to be a movie director!" said Steven. "Of course you will be!" said Mom. Even as a child, Steven Spielberg wanted to make movies. When he was 13, Steven won a contest for one of his movies. Later, Steven toured Universal Studios. He returned every day and pretended to work there. This is how he learned about the movie industry.

7. What is "Steven Spielberg: Movie Maker" mostly about?
   a. the early life of Steven Spielberg
   b. Steven Spielberg's greatest movies
   c. Steven Spielberg's parents
   d. Universal Studios

8. Dialogue is ____.
   a. the events in a text
   b. where an event happens
   c. what people say to each other
   d. an author's attitude about people in a text

9. Which sentence from the biography is dialogue?
   a. "Mom, I want to be a movie director!" said Steven.
   b. Later, Steven toured Universal Studios.
   c. Even as a child, Steven Spielberg wanted to make movies.
   d. He returned every day and pretended to work there.

10. What is the author's purpose in "Steven Spielberg: Movie Maker"?
    a. to entertain
    b. to inform
    c. to persuade
    d. to see movies

QUIZ Unit 4 • Chapter 3 *(continued)*

> **"Our Lake"**
>
> 1   Friends and neighbors! We must work together to clean up the lake. The lake is very important to our lives. We swim in its blue waters. We eat fish that live in its blue waters. If we do not preserve the lake, our children will be unable to enjoy it. It is our lake. Let us work together to save it!

---

11. "Our Lake" is a _____.
   a. legend
   b. biography
   c. speech
   d. play

12. Which words are repeated in "Our Lake"?
   a. preserve the lake
   b. friends and neighbors
   c. the lake is very important
   d. in its blue waters

13. A speech is _____.
   a. a made-up story
   b. never spoken aloud
   c. spoken aloud
   d. a type of poem

C. ➤ **Reading Strategies:** Choose the correct answer. *(16 points: 4 points each)*

14. When you _____, you use what you know to make a guess about what you read.
   a. determine sequence of events
   b. describe mental images
   c. proofread for errors
   d. draw inferences

15. Ramona has many books. You can infer that _____.
   a. Ramona likes to read.
   b. Ramona is often tired
   c. Ramona's mother works at a hospital
   d. Ramona has many videos.

16. Vincent laughed a lot at the party. You can infer that _____.
   a. Vincent saw a movie yesterday
   b. Vincent's mother drove him to the party
   c. Vincent had fun at the party
   d. Vincent goes to parties often

17. John is a kind person. What information could you use to draw this inference?
   a. John goes to bed late every night.
   b. John helps people after school.
   c. John wore blue jeans yesterday.
   d. Alan is John's best friend.

D. ➤ **Grammar/Usage:** Choose the correct answer. *(12 points: 4 points each)*

18. The word <u>let</u> is sometimes used to express _____.
   a. commands
   b. prefixes
   c. nouns
   d. characters

19. Which of these sentences is a command?
   a. All people like to be happy.
   b. Let all people be happy.
   c. People are not always happy.
   d. I read an article about happiness.

20. Let it rain! This sentence means _____.
   a. the speaker wants it to rain
   b. rain is better than snow
   c. the speaker wants the rain to end
   d. plants need rain to grow

E. ➤ **Writing** *(20 points)*

> **Writing Prompt** Think of something that needs to be changed in your neighborhood. Write a speech that asks people to work together to reach that goal.

QUIZ Unit 4 • Chapter 4

A. ➤ **Vocabulary:** Choose the correct answer. *(20 points: 4 points each)*

1. Making a web can help you _____.
   a. find information in a text
   b. remember new words
   c. understand chronology
   d. predict what will happen

---

diverge /dɪˈvɜrdʒ/ *-v* to separate and go in different directions

---

2. Which sentence uses <u>diverge</u> correctly?
   a. Marisol went to the diverge yesterday.
   b. They diverge the answers.
   c. My parents diverge their opinions about movies.
   d. The highway diverges into two smaller roads.

3. The suffix _____ means "a person who does something."
   a. *-ion*
   b. *-ly*
   c. *re-*
   d. *-er*

4. A _____ is a person who skates.
   a. skated
   b. skates
   c. skater
   d. skatier

5. A _____ is a person who drives.
   a. driver
   b. overdrive
   c. drived
   d. driving

B. ➤ **Text Structure/Elements of Literature:** Read and choose the correct answer. *(24 points: 4 points each)*

"When Evening Comes"

1 I love when evening comes
   A dancer in a soft blue dress
   And twinkling diamond earrings.

2 She invites me
   "Put to rest your daytime cares
   And dance with me for a while."

---

6. "When Evening Comes" has _____ stanzas.
   a. 1
   b. 2
   c. 3
   d. 4

7. What is this poem about?
   a. a blue dress
   b. diamond earrings
   c. feelings about the evening
   d. going to sleep

8. The poet uses the image of a dancer to show that _____.
   a. the poet enjoys the evening
   b. the daytime is better than the evening
   c. the poet is tired in the evening
   d. it often rains in the evening

"Acorns and Oak Trees"

1 When we are young, our only wish is to grow as tall as an oak tree in the woods.

2 When we are older, our only want is to be as young as a fresh acorn on a tree.

QUIZ Unit 4 • Chapter 4 *(continued)*

9. "Acorns and Oak Trees" a(n) ____.
   a. myth
   b. poem
   c. science fiction story
   d. informational text

10. The image of a tall oak tree shows that ____.
    a. children often hurry to grow up
    b. playing in the woods is fun
    c. oak trees are beautiful
    d. many children are tall

11. Which word is a first-person pronoun?
    a. when
    b. we
    c. are
    d. young

C. ➤ **Reading Strategies:** Choose the correct answer. *(16 points: 4 points each)*

12. To ____ is to show how two things are different.
    a. compare
    b. predict
    c. capitalize
    d. contrast

13. Colette and Gladys both have black hair. This is a ____.
    a. contrast
    b. definition
    c. comparison
    d. conclusion

14. Which sentence shows a contrast?
    a. My bicycle is big.
    b. Indra is older than Ana.
    c. Birds eat seeds.
    d. My mother is a doctor and so is your mother.

15. Which sentence shows a comparison?
    a. Both of our cats are fat.
    b. My room is cleaner than yours.
    c. We drive to class at night.
    d. It is raining today.

D. ➤ **Grammar/Usage:** Choose the correct answer. *(20 points: 4 points each)*

16. The actual words someone says is ____.
    a. reported speech
    b. exaggeration
    c. direct speech
    d. figurative language

17. ____ tells what someone else said.
    a. Direct speech
    b. Reported speech
    c. A comparative adjective
    d. Chronological order

18. Direct speech always uses ____.
    a. exclamation points
    b. past tense
    c. quotation marks
    d. compound words

19. Which sentence uses reported speech?
    a. The man said that he was ready.
    b. Nadja complains all the time.
    c. Can we leave?
    d. She said, "Yes, that is correct."

20. Carlo said, "Mom and I are moving to Maine." Which correctly rewrites this sentence as reported speech?
    a. Carlo said that he and Mom are moving to Maine.
    b. Mom said that she is moving to Maine.
    c. Carlo said that Mom is moving to Maine.
    d. Mom said that Carlo is moving to Maine.

E. ➤ **Writing** *(20 points)*

Writing Prompt Write a two-stanza poem about a person you admire. Use imagery to describe the person.

TEST • Unit 4

A. ➤ Reading

Visas for Life

1   "It's just a piece of paper," young Ruth thought as she waited in the long line for Mr. Sugihara's signature. Everyone in the line knew it meant much more. That little piece of paper was what would get her out of Europe before the Nazis could catch her.

"It" was a visa, and it meant the difference between life and death.

2   For a long time it seemed that no one would help the Jews. Polish Jews had been rounded up and sent to death camps. Some who escaped did so with the aid of one man. His name was Mr. Sugihara. He was in Lithuania working for the Japanese government. Even though he was told not to sign any visas, Mr. Sugihara was determined to save lives.

3   Mr. Sugihara wrote and wrote visas until his hands were sore. His wife, Yukiko, helped him. Sometimes she rubbed his hands to keep them from getting stiff. She even held his hand to help him form the letters. Unfortunately, time ran out and they had to leave. Ruth never forgot her last sight of the man who saved her life. He was already on the train, yet he was still signing visas. Finally, the train started to move. Mr. Sugihara stood up and bowed. He even apologized for not being able to sign any more visas.

4   Thousands of people escaped to Asia before heading to America. When they finally reached the United States, they started a new life. It would never have been possible without that one piece of paper. It couldn't have happened without one brave man who thought only of what he could do to help save lives.

TEST • Unit 4 *(continued)*

B. ➤ **Reading Comprehension:** Choose the correct answer. *(20 points: 2 points each)*

1. What is Ruth trying to get in "Visas for Life"?
   a. a card
   b. a visa
   c. a pen
   d. a light

2. Who helped Ruth in the story?
   a. Mr. Sugihara
   b. Ruth helped herself
   c. The government
   d. Her friends

3. Who is Ruth trying to get away from?
   a. her friends
   b. Yukiko
   c. the Nazis
   d. the Japanese

4. What motivated Mr. Sugihara to sign visas?
   a. He liked to write.
   b. He had many friends.
   c. He wanted to save lives.
   d. The government told him to sign visas.

5. Ruth is grateful to Mr. Sugihara because she thinks he _____.
   a. visited her family
   b. was her teacher
   c. was a happy person
   d. saved her life

6. Why did Mr. Sugihara feel bad at the end of the story?
   a. He had to stay.
   b. He couldn't sign any more visas.
   c. He felt like going on a trip.
   d. He wanted to get a visa.

7. A visa is a _____ that allows you to enter another country.
   a. piece of paper
   b. coin
   c. booklet
   d. pen

8. What two words describe Ruth?
   a. pretty and warm
   b. thankful and determined
   c. small and active
   d. selfish and young

9. What two words describe Mr. Sugihara?
   a. mean and hungry
   b. helpless and selfish
   c. helpful and selfless
   d. ambitious and strange

10. Yukiko is most likely _____ Mr. Sugihara.
    a. angry with
    b. proud of
    c. discouraged by
    d. embarrassed by

TEST • Unit 4 (continued)

C. ➤ Reading Strategies: Choose the correct answer. *(10 points: 2 points each)*

11. If Mr. Sugihara could have stayed in Lithuania longer, he would have saved more lives. This is _____.
    a. imagery
    b. a prediction
    c. a simile
    d. personification

12. Which happened first in "Visas for Life"?
    a. Mr. Sugihara left Lithuania
    b. Yukiko held his sore hands
    c. Ruth's mother said, "Hello."
    d. Ruth stood in line for a visa.

13. Which happened last in "Visas for Life"?
    a. Mr. Sugihara signed Ruth's visa.
    b. Yukiko held Mr. Sugihara's sore hands.
    c. Ruth waited in the long line.
    d. Mr Sugihara apologized for not being able to sign any more visas.

14. Ruth thought that Mr. Sugihara saved her life. You can guess that others felt the same way as Ruth. This is _____.
    a. a prediction
    b. an inference
    c. a summary
    d. a main idea

15. Which of the following is a comparison between Mr. Sugihara and Ruth?
    a. Mr Sugihara helped people.
    b. Mr. Sugihara is Japanese, but Ruth is Jewish.
    c. Mr. Sugihara and Ruth were both in Lithuania.
    d. Mr. Sugihara is old, and Ruth is young.

D. ➤ Elements of Literature: Choose the correct answer. *(10 points: 2 points each)*

16. The main characters in "Visas for Life" are _____.
    a. the Nazis
    b. Ruth and Yukiko
    c. Yukiko and her daughter
    d. Mr. Sugihara and Ruth

17. Who is the minor character in "Visas for Life"?
    a. Ruth
    b. Mr. Sugihara
    c. Yukiko
    d. a girl

18. "Visas for Life" is told from the _____ point of view.
    a. fourth-person
    b. first-person
    c. second-person
    d. third-person

19. In third-person point of view the narrator is _____.
    a. a character in the story
    b. not a character in the story
    c. always talking in the story
    d. the main character

20. Which sentence from "Visas for Life" is an example of imagery?
    a. She waited in the long line.
    b. The man was willing to help.
    c. Instead, they ordered him to leave the country.
    d. Even so, time ran out.

TEST • Unit 4 (continued)

E. ➤ Vocabulary: Choose the correct answer. *(10 points: 2 points each)*

21. She even held his hands to help him <u>form</u> the letters. What does *form* mean?
    a. a piece of paper
    b. write
    c. eat
    d. send

22. Which of the following words has a suffix?
    a. walk
    b. help
    c. helper
    d. hand

23. Unfortunately, time ran out and they had to leave. Which word has a suffix?
    a. Unfortunately
    b. time
    c. ran
    d. leave

24. Which of the following words has a prefix that means "not"?
    a. unpack
    b. portray
    c. retry
    d. repay

25. When a suffix is added to the end of a word, it changes ____ of the word.
    a. the humor
    b. the meaning
    c. the style
    d. the beauty

F. ➤ Grammar/Usage: Choose the correct answer. *(10 points: 2 points each)*

26. People use the word *let* to ____.
    a. show imagery
    b. express a command
    c. express a fact
    d. make an inference

27. A prepositional phrase of time tells ____.
    a. where something happened
    b. who did something
    c. when something happened
    d. why something happened

28. Which sentence has a prepositional phrase?
    a. Jill went to Mexico on Saturday.
    b. Joe admired Mr. Kelley.
    c. Maurice helped Mrs. Loinaz.
    d. Mr. Rock signed papers.

29. Miss Pardo says that she will sign the visas. This is an example of ____ speech.
    a. direct
    b. loud
    c. quiet
    d. reported

30. Which of the following sets of words are prepositions?
    a. you, me, he, she
    b. the, it, we
    c. in, at, on, over
    d. grass, land, water

TEST • Unit 4 *(continued)*

G. ➤ **Writing Conventions:** Choose the correct answer. *(10 points: 2 points each)*

31. Andrew _____ on Mr. Henderson's door. Which word best completes the sentence?
 a. nocked
 b. knocked
 c. ncked
 d. knoked

32. The correct way to spell 25 in a sentence is _____.
 a. twentyfive
 b. twenty five
 c. twenty-five
 d. 25

33. When they finally reached the United States, they started a new life. Which word has the long /u/ sound like in the word blue?
 a. finally
 b. reached
 c. started
 d. new

34. Which sentence uses correct punctuation?
 a. Boston, which is a busy city is fun to visit.
 b. Give the paper to your teacher Ms. Carza.
 c. Our coach, who is new, likes to play soccer.
 d. Our neighbors who are very nice, have a beautiful garden.

35. What letter is silent in the word watch?
 a. w
 b. a
 c. t
 d. ch

H. ➤ **Editing:** Read and choose the correct answer. *(10 points: 2 points each)*

"Ariana"

(1) Ariana are always reading. (2) Her spends all of her free time at the library. (3) While reading, she learns a lot about many different topics. (4) As a result, she does well in all of her subjects at school. (5) Arianas favorite subjects are science and English. (6) She wants to be a doctor someday?

---

36. What change should you make to sentence 1?
 a. change *are* to *is*
 b. move *always* after *reading*
 c. change the period to a question mark
 d. make no change

37. What change should you make to sentence 2?
 a. change *Her* to *She*
 b. change *spends* to *spend*
 c. change *library* to *libary*
 d. make no change

38. What change should you make to sentence 4?
 a. change *does* to *do*
 b. change *her* to *hers*
 c. change *subjects* to *subject*
 d. make no change

39. What change should you make to sentence 5?
 a. change *Arianas* to *Ariana's*
 b. change *science* to *Science*
 c. change *English* to *english*
 d. make no change

TEST • Unit 4 *(continued)*

40. What change should you make to sentence 6?
   a. change *wants* to *want*
   b. change *doctor* to *Doctor*
   c. change the question mark to a period
   d. make no change

I. ➤ **Writing** *(20 points)*

> **Writing Prompt** Suppose you are Mr. Sugihara. You have just returned to Japan. All of your neighbors want to hear about the amazing work you have done. Write a speech explaining your work and the effect it has had on the lives of others. Use the Planning Guide to help you write.

Planning Guide
❏ On a separate sheet of paper, list Mr. Sughihara's achievements in Lithuania.
❏ List details about his work in helping the Jews.
❏ Write ideas about how he thinks everyone should help people who need it.
❏ Use your details and ideas to write your speech.
❏ Check your writing for spelling, punctuation, and capitalization.

Name _____ Date _____

Grade

QUIZ Unit 5 • Chapter 1

A. ➤ **Vocabulary:** Choose the correct answer. *(28 points: 4 points each)*

1. Nearby words and sentences are called _____.
   a. rhyme
   b. context
   c. pronunciation
   d. glossary

2. _____ have the same pronunciation but different meanings and spellings.
   a. Opinions
   b. Prefixes
   c. Homophones
   d. Verbs

3. I feel great today! In this sentence, great means _____.
   a. very good
   b. rub together
   c. a metal frame
   d. annoy

4. You like sports, and he does, _____.
   a. two
   b. to
   c. too
   d. tu

5. Compound adjectives _____.
   a. contain one word
   b. join verbs
   c. contain more than one word
   d. join two sentences

6. Tom was an eight-pound baby boy. What is the compound adjective?
   a. Tom
   b. eight-pound
   c. baby
   d. baby boy

7. She is wearing _____ boots. Complete this sentence with the compound adjective.
   a. nice
   b. tall, black
   c. dirty and old
   d. pointy-toed

B. ➤ **Text Structure/Elements of Literature:** Read and choose the correct answer. *(20 points: 4 points each)*

> "The New Porch"
>
> 1   Last year, Joshua and I rebuilt our front porch. The porch was very old and the wood was as soft as a rotten apple. We used large hammers to break up the old wood. Then, we cleared it away and constructed the new porch out of fresh wood. We worked for hours on our knees. My back felt as tight as a taut rubber band, but the porch looked fantastic.

8. "The New Porch" is a _____.
   a. personal narrative
   b. historical play
   c. textbook article
   d. nonfiction article

9. The purpose of "The New Porch" is to _____.
   a. describe an event that happened to another person
   b. tell about made-up characters
   c. describe an event that happened to the author
   d. explain how to rebuild a porch

10. A simile _____.
    a. shows how two things are different
    b. is a group of letters added to the end of a word
    c. lists words with similar meanings
    d. shows how two things are similar

QUIZ Unit 5 • Chapter 1 (continued)

11. Which sentence from the reading contains a simile?
    a. Last year, Joshua and I rebuilt our front porch.
    b. My back felt as tight as a taut rubber band.
    c. We worked for hours on our knees.
    d. But the porch looked fantastic.

12. The wood was as soft as a rotten apple. This sentence means that _____.
    a. the wood was very soft
    b. the wood smelled very bad
    c. the wood was red
    d. the apple tasted bad

C. ➤ Reading Strategies: Choose the correct answer. *(12 points: 4 points each)*

13. When you draw conclusions, you _____.
    a. rewrite a paragraph in your own words
    b. find details to support the main idea
    c. use word squares to remember new words
    d. use what you know to determine how someone thinks or feels

14. Carmen watched a scary movie and could not sleep. You can conclude that _____.
    a. Carmen worked all day
    b. the movie was old
    c. the movie scared Carmen
    d. it was cold that night

15. Andy studied hard and got an A. You can conclude that _____.
    a. Andy is mad at his friend
    b. Andy is happy
    c. the test was difficult
    d. Andy is bored

D. ➤ Grammar/Usage: Choose the correct answer. *(20 points: 4 points each)*

16. The _____ describes actions that happened already.
    a. future tense
    b. present tense
    c. past tense
    d. present participle

17. Which verb is regular?
    a. was
    b. called
    c. grew
    d. gave

18. Which verb is irregular?
    a. dove
    b. chewed
    c. opened
    d. picked

19. Last week, Asa _____ a great picture of me.
    a. drawing
    b. drawed
    c. draw
    d. drew

20. I _____ at work all day yesterday.
    a. is
    b. was
    c. were
    d. am

E. ➤ Writing *(20 points)*

Writing Prompt Write a personal narrative about a time when you explored a new place. Use similes to describe what you saw and how you felt.

Name _____ Date _____

Grade

QUIZ Unit 5 • Chapter 2

A. ➤ Vocabulary: Choose the correct answer. *(24 points: 4 points each)*

1. _____ are words used to make other words.
   a. Homonyms
   b. Prefixes
   c. Suffixes
   d. Root words

---

line /laɪn/ *noun* **1** a long mark made with a pen or pencil **2** a group of people standing one behind the other **3** a wrinkle on the face **4** a short written message

---

2. I drew a line on the paper. Which definition matches the word line in this sentence?
   a. definition 1
   b. definition 2
   c. definition 3
   d. definition 4

3. The word *funny* means "humorous." *Funny* can also mean _____.
   a. smile
   b. strange
   c. feeling
   d. laugh

4. The English word spectator comes from the Latin root word *specere,* meaning "to look." Spectator means _____.
   a. a car with four doors
   b. moving quickly
   c. a person who watches an event
   d. a cold, winter day

5. The English word demonstration comes from a Latin root word that means "to show." Demonstration means _____.
   a. the act of destroying something
   b. the act of showing something
   c. the act of creating something
   d. the act of completing something

6. I rush when I am late for school. In this sentence, rush means _____.
   a. move quickly
   b. a type of plant
   c. carry a football
   d. capture a person or place

B. ➤ Text Structure/Elements of Literature: Read and choose the correct answer. *(16 points: 4 points each)*

"Cars"

1   "Mom, what were cars like when you were young?" Ari's mother smiled as she flew her car to the store. "Well," she said, "people didn't fly cars through the air like we do today. They drove cars on the ground." Ari shook his head in disbelief. "Wow! Things were so different back then."

---

7. Setting is _____.
   a. where and when a story happens
   b. the most important event in a story
   c. characters in a story
   d. pictures you form in your mind

8. Most science fiction stories are set in _____.
   a. a house
   b. the future
   c. the present
   d. the past

9. In "Cars," Ari and his mother are _____.
   a. in a car
   b. at the grocery store
   c. at home
   d. in a park

QUIZ Unit 5 • Chapter 2 (continued)

10. _____ is a made-up story based on scientific information.
    a. Historical fiction
    b. Informational text
    c. Personal narrative
    d. Science fiction

C. ➤ Reading Strategies: Choose the correct answer. (16 points: 4 points each)

11. When you _____, you use text clues and your experience to understand a story.
    a. analyze cause and effect
    b. determine sequence of events
    c. distinguish fact from opinion
    d. draw inferences

12. Kai's hair is wet, and she is wearing a bathing suit. You can infer that _____.
    a. it is Monday
    b. Kai is going to the doctor
    c. Kai went swimming
    d. Kai's bathing suit is green

13. Michael fell off his bicycle. Which evidence supports this inference?
    a. Michael is late for school.
    b. Michael has cuts on his knees.
    c. Many children are playing outside.
    d. It is Michael's birthday

14. The sky is gray. You can infer that _____.
    a. it will rain soon
    b. it is a holiday
    c. there are many planes in the sky
    d. gray is the author's favorite color

D. ➤ Grammar/Usage: Choose the correct answer. (24 points: 4 points each)

15. A _____ is part of a sentence with a subject and verb.
    a. pronoun
    b. thesaurus
    c. prefix
    d. clause

16. A(n) _____ can stand on its own.
    a. independent clause
    b. informational text
    c. dependent clause
    d. homophone

17. A(n) _____ cannot stand on its own.
    a. contraction
    b. independent clause
    c. dependent clause
    d. passive voice

18. I am excited because today is my birthday. The dependent clause is _____.
    a. I am excited
    b. my birthday
    c. today is my birthday
    d. because today is my birthday

19. Which sentence contains both an independent and a dependent clause?
    a. I locked the door because I left.
    b. I locked the door and I left.
    c. The bird sang.
    d. The bird sang a song and flew away.

20. The plant grew. It got a lot of sunshine. How can you combine these two sentences using <u>because</u>?
    a. Because the plant grew and it got a lot of sunshine.
    b. The plant grew because it got a lot of sunshine.
    c. The plant and sunshine grew a lot because.
    d. The plant grew because so did the sunshine.

E. ➤ Writing (20 points)

> **Writing Prompt** Write a science fiction story about a person who explores a new place. Include details to describe the setting.

Name _____ Date _____

Grade

QUIZ Unit 5 • Chapter 3

A. ➤ Vocabulary: Choose the correct answer. *(20 points: 4 points each)*

---
optimism /ˈɑptəˌmɪzəm/ *n.* the belief that good things will happen: *He is filled with optimism; he believes that he will win the award.*

---

1. Which underlined phrase matches the definition of optimism?
   a. I dream about traveling to other countries.
   b. You think that everything will be all right.
   c. My mother creates beautiful works of art.
   d. Tom worries about everything.

---
sensitive /ˈsɛnsətɪv/ *adj.* easily hurt or affected emotionally: *Juan is sensitive; be careful not to hurt his feelings.*

---

2. Which underlined phrase most closely matches the definition of sensitive?
   a. She spends little time doing her work.
   b. Kaya does not believe that her brother lied.
   c. Lane has hurt feelings because you don't like the food.
   d. He is confused all the time.

3. The word microscope comes from the Greek word *skop*, which means "to look at." Microscope means _____.
   a. a car or truck
   b. an old story about a hero
   c. to move from one side to the other
   d. a tool for seeing very small objects

4. The word telegraph contains the Greek word *tele*, which means "far." Telegraph means _____.
   a. sends messages to distant places
   b. just happened today
   c. a time when many people lose their jobs
   d. a tool for hunting large animals

5. The word chronology means "the order that events occur." Chronology comes from the Greek word *chrónos*, which means _____.
   a. time
   b. happiness
   c. city
   d. paper

B. ➤ Text Structure/Elements of Literature: Read and choose the correct answer. *(28 points: 4 points each)*

"Earth's Rocks"

1 Do you know that Earth has three kinds of rocks?
   1. *igneous:* form from cooling **magma** (melted rock)
   2. *sedimentary:* form from rocks or minerals pressed together
   3. *metamorphic:* form when rocks are under very strong heat or pressure, causing the minerals in the rocks to become new minerals

---

6. "Earth's Rocks" is a(n) _____.
   a. short story
   b. informational text
   c. historical narrative
   d. autobiographical poem

7. Bold type, italic type, and numbered lists are _____.
   a. reference sources
   b. figurative language
   c. graphic features
   d. facts and opinions

8. The main topic of this reading is _____.
   a. the three types of rocks on Earth
   b. the names of sedimentary rocks
   c. the types of rocks on other planets
   d. how igneous rocks form

79

Name _____ Date _____

QUIZ Unit 5 • Chapter 3 (continued)

9. In "Earth's Rocks," the bold type is used to _____.
   a. ask a question
   b. signal a new word
   c. give an opinion
   d. begin a paragraph

10. _____ is how authors use language to express themselves.
   a. Mood
   b. Punctuation
   c. Homonym
   d. Style

11. In direct address, authors _____.
   a. describe events that happened to them
   b. speak directly to readers
   c. define words
   d. describe steps in a process

12. Which sentence uses direct address?
   a. We are going out to dinner tonight.
   b. Vicente painted the house all day.
   c. You may have heard his name before.
   d. The cows in the field ate grass.

C. ➤ Reading Strategies: Choose the correct answer. (20 points: 4 points each)

13. The _____ is why something happens.
   a. cause
   b. setting
   c. organization
   d. diagram

14. The effect is _____.
   a. what characters say in a text
   b. the main idea of a text
   c. what happens because of the cause
   d. two words with opposite meanings

15. The streets flooded because of the storm. In this sentence, the effect is that _____.
   a. there was a storm
   b. people were scared
   c. houses got wet
   d. the streets flooded

16. I am out of breath. A cause of this sentence might be _____.
   a. I woke up.
   b. I ran ten miles.
   c. I read a magazine.
   d. I smiled at the child.

17. You answered all of the questions correctly. The effect of this sentence might be _____.
   a. you bought a new jacket
   b. you picked flowers at the park
   c. you cleaned your room
   d. you did well on the science test

D. ➤ Grammar/Usage: Choose the correct answer. (12 points: 4 points each)

18. He might go home. In this sentence, might means _____.
   a. it is possible
   b. never
   c. cannot
   d. definitely

19. Which sentence is correct?
   a. Aaron might liked the movie.
   b. Aaron might liking the movie.
   c. Aaron might like the movie.
   d. Aaron might is liking the movie.

20. Yolanda might _____ at the party.
   a. is
   b. be
   c. was
   d. were

E. ➤ Writing (20 points)

Writing Prompt Write an informational text. Explain how to play your favorite game or sport step by step.

Name _____ Date _____

Grade

QUIZ Unit 5 • Chapter 4

A. ➤ Vocabulary: Choose the correct answer. *(20 points: 4 points each)*

1. To find a synonym, use a _____.
   a. biography
   b. thesaurus
   c. novel
   d. glossary

2. A _____ lists the chapters of a book.
   a. synonym finder
   b. dictionary
   c. textbook
   d. table of contents

3. You can use _____ to find a dictionary or thesaurus.
   a. an inference
   b. the Internet
   c. contractions
   d. adjectives

4. A _____ is two vowels that are pronounced as one vowel.
   a. diphthong
   b. noun
   c. suffix
   d. verb

5. The *oo* sound in the word *tool* can be heard in the word _____.
   a. good
   b. foot
   c. cool
   d. book

B. ➤ Text Structure/Elements of Literature: Read and choose the correct answer. *(20 points: 4 points each)*

> "The Story of European Painting"
>
> 1 **Cubism Takes Hold in Paris**
> Before 1907, most European painting was **realistic** (tried to reproduce the world as it looked). This changed when **Cubism** was created in Paris. Cubist artists painted flat, geometric shapes such as cubes rather than producing realistic images. Pablo Picasso was a famous Cubist painter.

6. "Cubism Takes Hold in Paris" is the _____.
   a. subtitle
   b. title of the text
   c. chart
   d. first sentence in the paragraph

7. What is the main topic of the reading?
   a. Pablo Picasso
   b. Paris
   c. Cubism
   d. realistic painting

8. "The Story of European Painting" is a(n) _____.
   a. myth
   b. historical narrative
   c. informational text
   d. speech

9. A _____ is a picture that helps you understand a text.
   a. paragraph
   b. fact
   c. figurative language
   d. graphic aid

10. A _____ is an example of a graphic aid.
    a. verb   c. dialogue
    b. photo   d. summary

81

QUIZ *Unit 5 • Chapter 4* *(continued)*

C. ➤ **Reading Strategies:** Choose the correct answer. *(16 points: 4 points each)*

11. To summarize is to _____.
    a. use what you know to make a guess
    b. notice how two things are different
    c. use a dictionary to find a definition
    d. write down the most important ideas in a text

12. Last summer was tough for Jorge. His dog ran away and he lost his job. He also broke his arm! Which sentence summarizes this paragraph?
    a. Jorge is a nice person.
    b. Jorge had a bad summer.
    c. Jorge lost his dog.
    d. Jorge got hurt last summer.

13. Why do I like to dance? First of all, I get to listen to music. Dancing is also great exercise. Finally, it just makes me feel good! Which sentence contains the main idea of this paragraph?
    a. the first sentence
    b. the second sentence
    c. the third sentence
    d. the fourth sentence

14. Ali's party was fun! There was a band and everyone went swimming. Which sentence summarizes this paragraph?
    a. Ali has a swimming pool.
    b. Ali plays in a band.
    c. Ali had a great party.
    d. Ali is my friend.

D. ➤ **Grammar/Usage:** Choose the correct answer. *(24 points: 4 points each)*

15. Superlative adjectives _____.
    a. compare three or more nouns
    b. describe action words
    c. describe events already happened
    d. join two sentences

16. Which word is a superlative adjective?
    a. loudly
    b. louder
    c. loud
    d. loudest

17. That is the _____ cat I have ever seen!
    a. cuter
    b. cutest
    c. cutiest
    d. cuted

18. She is the _____ person I know.
    a. nicest
    b. niced
    c. nicer
    d. nices

19. Laura is the tallest person in the room. This sentence compares Laura with _____.
    a. the room
    b. tall people
    c. everyone in the room
    d. her parents

20. Jupiter is the largest planet in the solar system. This sentence means that _____.
    a. other planets in the solar system are larger than Jupiter
    b. Jupiter is bigger than all planets in the solar system
    c. Jupiter is bigger than some planets in the solar system
    d. Jupiter is a very small planet

E. ➤ **Writing** *(20 points)*

Writing Prompt Your friend wants to learn about your school. Write an informational text that describes the events of a typical school day.

Grade

TEST • Unit 5

A. ➤ Reading

Journey from the Center of Earth

1   Have you ever kicked a rock down the street? You might even have thought, "Until I came along, this rock never moved." You would be wrong. It had already been on an unbelievable journey.

Igneous Rocks

2   An igneous rock begins its long journey deep inside Earth. If you could go to the center of Earth, this is what you would find. The deeper it is, the hotter the temperature. In fact, the word *igneous* comes from the Latin word for fire.

3   It is hottest at the center, so rock material melts and flows like a river. This melted material is called **magma.** Sometimes magma rises to the surface of Earth. It flows out of deep cracks in Earth. Or it comes from a volcano. When magma reaches the surface, it is called **lava.**

Extrusive Rocks

4   Some igneous rocks are extrusive. This means they form on the surface of Earth. When lava reaches the surface, it solidifies because it is much cooler there. It becomes solid, or hard, the way water does when it freezes. Ice is solid water.

Texture of Igneous Rocks

5   What kind of ice cream do you like? One kind might be chunky with bits of candy and nuts in it. The other might be smooth with no extras. When you describe ice cream this way, you are describing its texture.

6   You might say the texture of a rock is like that, too. However, the bits and pieces are called *particles.* The particles in an igneous rock are mineral crystals. When lava cools slowly, the crystals have time to grow bigger. When lava cools fast, the crystals are smaller. In fact, you might not see them at all.

TEST • Unit 5 *(continued)*

B. ➤ **Reading Comprehension:** Choose the correct answer. *(20 points: 2 points each)*

1. In writing, what marks surround dialogue or a thought?
   a. commas
   b. question marks
   c. quotation marks
   d. periods

2. Where does an igneous rock begin its long journey?
   a. in the sky
   b. on a plateau
   c. in a lake
   d. inside Earth

3. Where is Earth the hottest?
   a. in the crack
   b. in the center
   c. around the outside
   d. on top of it

4. What is the melted material in the center of Earth called?
   a. soil
   b. magma
   c. hot stuff
   d. igneous

5. Where do extrusive rocks form?
   a. in the middle of Earth
   b. underwater
   c. high in the air
   d. on the surface of Earth

6. When lava cools fast, the crystals are _____.
   a. big
   b. small
   c. orange
   d. green

7. The particles in the igneous rock are _____.
   a. candy and nuts
   b. magma
   c. mineral crystals
   d. textures

8. When lava reaches the surface of Earth it _____.
   a. moves
   b. turns to water
   c. evaporates
   d. solidifies

9. The word *igneous* comes from the Latin word for _____.
   a. air
   b. rock
   c. rain
   d. fire

10. Bits and pieces of rock are called _____.
   a. particles
   b. air
   c. rocks
   d. extrusive

TEST • Unit 5 (continued)

C. ➤ **Reading Strategies:** Choose the correct answer. *(10 points: 2 points each)*

11. Summarize "Journey from the Center of Earth."
    a. Most rocks are formed in the center of Earth.
    b. The center of Earth is hot.
    c. The center of Earth is cold.
    d. It is fun to travel to the center of Earth.

12. A rock solidifies because the surface of Earth is cooler. What is the effect in this sentence?
    a. Earth is cooler.
    b. A rock solidifies.
    c. Magma is formed.
    d. A rock needs heat.

13. When lava cools slowly, the crystals grow bigger. What is the cause in this sentence?
    a. The lava cools.
    b. The lava cools slowly.
    c. The crystals grow.
    d. The crystals grow bigger.

14. From reading "Journey from the Center of Earth," a reader can infer that _____.
    a. it is too hot to touch the center of Earth
    b. it would be fun to play in the center of Earth
    c. Earth's surface is hot
    d. Earth is cold in the middle

15. You can infer that the author of "Journey from the Center of Earth" _____.
    a. knows nothing about rocks
    b. knows a lot about rocks and where they came from
    c. is not very interested in rocks
    d. has traveled to the center of the Earth

D. ➤ **Elements of Literature:** Choose the correct answer. *(10 points: 2 points each)*

16. The setting of "Journey from the Center of Earth" is _____.
    a. in Earth
    b. at school
    c. in a large city
    d. in a park

17. An example of figurative language in "Journey from the Center of Earth" is _____.
    a. the part about magma
    b. the part about ice cream
    c. the part about the lava
    d. the part about rocks

18. The picture of the volcano supports the idea that _____.
    a. magma flows like a river
    b. Earth's center is cool
    c. eruptions rarely occur
    d. magma is cool

19. "Have you ever kicked a rock down the street?" This is an example of a(n) _____.
    a. report
    b. direct address
    c. answer
    d. indirect address

20. Graphic aids help readers _____.
    a. read faster
    b. draw
    c. understand new information
    d. write longer books

TEST • Unit 5 *(continued)*

E. ➤ **Vocabulary:** Choose the correct answer. *(10 points: 2 points each)*

21. "You might say the texture of a rock is like that, too." Which word in the sentence rhymes with the word <u>do</u>?
    a. you
    b. might
    c. say
    d. that

22. What is the meaning of <u>extrusive</u>?
    a. formed into particles
    b. solidified
    c. formed on Earth's surface
    d. igneous rock

23. Which of the following is an example of a compound adjective?
    a. peanut-sized
    b. ice cream
    c. popcorn
    d. inside

24. The words <u>way</u> and <u>weigh</u> are _____.
    a. adjectives
    b. nouns
    c. homophones
    d. purple words

25. A(n) _____ is a part of a book that gives the meanings of words.
    a. index
    b. glossary
    c. table of contents
    d. bibliography

F. ➤ **Grammar/Usage** *(10 points: 2 points each)*

26. It is possible that you will go to the park. Which is the best way to restate this sentence?
    a. You are going to the park.
    b. You might go to the park.
    c. You always go to the park.
    d. There is no way you are going to the park.

27. The simple past tense describes actions that began and ended _____.
    a. in the present
    b. in school
    c. in the road
    d. in the past

28. Arturo wanted to read the book <u>because he wanted to learn about reptiles.</u> The underlined phrase is _____.
    a. an independent clause
    b. a complete sentence
    c. a dependent clause
    d. a definition

29. Which of the following is a dependent clause?
    a. because I want to be healthy
    b. I will run
    c. I want to be healthy
    d. I play the guitar

30. Complete the sentence. "Greg is the _____ runner in his class."
    a. fast
    b. faster
    c. fastest
    d. quick

TEST • Unit 5 *(continued)*

G. ➤ **Writing Conventions:** Choose the correct answer. *(10 points: 2 points each)*

31. Which letters in the word *rough* make the /f/ sound?
    a. f
    b. ou
    c. ph
    d. gh

32. Which is the correct way to write the first month of the year?
    a. jan
    b. Janu
    c. january
    d. January

33. The bag belongs to Raul. Whose bag is it?
    a. It is Raul.
    b. It is Raul bag.
    c. It is Rauls bag.
    d. It is Raul's bag.

34. The names of planets should be _____.
    a. italicized
    b. underlined
    c. capitalized
    d. bold-faced

35. To make the word <u>paradox</u> plural, add _____.
    a. s
    b. es
    c. en
    d. ed

H. ➤ **Editing:** Choose the correct answer. *(10 points: 2 points each)*

"Telephones"

(1) Telephones are a very common way to communicate, (2) They are easy to use. (3) Many people uses them to keep in touch with their family and friends who are far away. (4) In the telephone, you can talk to people on the other side of the world. (5) Maybe someday we will use telephones to talk to people on mars.

---

36. What change should you make to sentence 1?
    a. change *are* to *is*
    b. add a comma between *very* and *common*
    c. change the comma to a period
    d. make no change

37. What change should you make to sentence 2?
    a. change *They* to *Them*
    b. change *are* to *is*
    c. change *to use* to *use*
    d. make no change

38. What change should you make to sentence 3?
    a. change *uses* to *use*
    b. change *them* to *they*
    c. change *to keep* to *keeping*
    d. make no change

39. What change should you make to sentence 4?
    a. change *In* to *On*
    b. change *can* to *could*
    c. change *world* to *World*
    d. make no change

TEST • Unit 5 *(continued)*

40. What change should you make to sentence 5?
  a. change *Maybe* to *Might*
  b. change *will* to *use*
  c. change *mars* to *Mars*
  d. make no change

I. ➤ **Writing** *(20 points)*

> **Writing Prompt** Choose one thing you know how to do well. Write three paragraphs explaining the steps in the process. Include an introduction and step-by-step instructions. Use the Planning Guide to help you write.

Planning Guide
❑ List the steps in the process.
❑ Use details and explain each step clearly.
❑ Write an introduction.
❑ Check your writing for spelling, punctuation, and capitalization.

QUIZ Unit 6 • Chapter 1

A. ➤ Vocabulary: Choose the correct answer. *(28 points: 4 points each)*

1. Everyone likes my father because he is <u>affable</u>. <u>Affable</u> means _____.
   a. pleasant
   b. old
   c. boring
   d. horrible

2. We want to stay inside because the sky is <u>overcast</u>. <u>Overcast</u> means _____.
   a. bright blue
   b. filled with stars
   c. gray and cloudy
   d. sunny and warm

> **ingenious** /ɪn'dʒinyəs/ *adj.* very good at making things or solving problems, clever: *She is an ingenious chef who creates new and exciting dishes.*

3. Which underlined word has a similar meaning as ingenious?
   a. Mona is an <u>imaginative</u> writer who develops great stories.
   b. The <u>irritated</u> man told her to leave him alone.
   c. The old house was <u>drafty</u> and cold.
   d. Liem is a <u>dedicated</u> person who works hard.

4. Denotative meanings are _____.
   a. opposite meanings
   b. dictionary meanings
   c. incorrect meanings
   d. similar meanings

5. Connotative meanings are _____.
   a. dictionary meanings
   b. feelings you get from a word
   c. meanings that rhyme
   d. prefixes and suffixes

6. They <u>declare</u> you the winner! The denotative meaning of <u>declare</u> is _____.
   a. to be quiet
   b. to be important
   c. to sit down
   d. to announce

7. She <u>draped</u> the scarf around her neck. A connotative meaning of <u>draped</u> is _____.
   a. let go of
   b. hung
   c. hung beautifully
   d. fell noisely

B. ➤ Text Structure/Elements of Literature: Read and choose the correct answer. *(16 points: 4 points each)*

> "Who's Afraid of Dogs?"
>
> 1 Fatima was afraid of dogs. One day, she was walking to school when she noticed a dog running toward her. Fatima was so frightened that she could not move. Instead of attacking her, the dog began licking Fatima's hand. He wanted to play! Fatima smiled and petted the dog's head. From then on, she was no longer afraid of dogs.

8. In the reading, one of Fatima's character traits is that she is _____.
   a. afraid of dogs
   b. a good student
   c. friendly to cats
   d. a fast runner

9. _____ is the reason a character does something.
   a. Plot
   b. Setting
   c. Character change
   d. Character motivation

QUIZ Unit 6 • Chapter 1 (continued)

10. How does Fatima change in the reading?
  a. She goes to a new school.
  b. She stops being afraid of dogs.
  c. She becomes afraid of dogs.
  d. She learns to ride a bike.

11. In this reading, the plot is _____.
  a. Fatima loses her fear of dogs
  b. the dog likes people
  c. Fatima is late for school
  d. Fatima gets a new pet

C. ➤ Reading Strategies: Choose the correct answer. *(16 points: 4 points each)*

12. To _____ is to use text information and your experience to guess.
  a. analyze cause and effect
  b. use word origins
  c. make inferences
  d. compare two different things

13. Irma raises her hand after her teacher asks a question. You can infer that _____.
  a. it is January
  b. Irma likes her teacher
  c. Irma is in reading class
  d. Irma knows the answer

14. Manny seems worried as he looks at his watch. You can infer that _____.
  a. Manny is driving a car
  b. Manny is late
  c. Manny's mother bought him the watch
  d. Manny is going to a movie

15. You infer that Linda liked her dinner. Which statement supports this inference?
  a. Linda ate everything on her plate.
  b. Linda is wearing jeans.
  c. It is 9:00 P.M.
  d. Linda ate spaghetti.

D. ➤ Grammar/Usage: Choose the correct answer. *(20 points: 4 points each)*

16. A possessive adjective _____.
  a. describes an action
  b. is an author's attitude toward a character
  c. explains where an event happens
  d. shows who or what owns an object

17. Which is the possessive adjective?
  a. the
  b. our
  c. we
  d. am

18. What is the possessive adjective for *I*?
  a. my
  b. your
  c. his
  d. their

19. Maya put on _____ coat. Complete the sentence with the possessive adjective.
  a. the
  b. a
  c. her
  d. she

20. The monkey ate _____ banana. Complete the sentence with the possessive adjective.
  a. no
  b. it's
  c. its
  d. the

E. ➤ Writing *(20 points)*

Writing Prompt Write a fictional short story about someone who makes a change in his or her life. Describe why and how this person made the change.

QUIZ Unit 6 • Chapter 2

A. ➤ **Vocabulary:** Choose the correct answer. *(24 points: 4 points each)*

1. Tamika is very happy. She feels ____.
   a. guilty
   b. joyful
   c. confident
   d. confused

2. Jaime is ____. He does not know if he should stay or go.
   a. guilty
   b. joyful
   c. confident
   d. confused

3. Which sentence describes a person who feels guilty?
   a. Jean feels badly because she took a book without asking.
   b. Sun-Hee laughs at the funny story.
   c. Eduardo is crying because his friend moved away.
   d. Anja is excited because her mother got a new car.

4. Words with similar meanings are called ____.
   a. subjects
   b. commas
   c. synonyms
   d. predictions

5. You can use a(n) ____ to find a synonym.
   a. autobiography
   b. thesaurus
   c. metaphor
   d. image

   ┌───┐
   implore *verb* beg, beseech, entreat, plead; *antonym:* do not ask for
   └───┘

6. In this thesaurus entry, what is a synonym for implore?
   a. want
   b. steal
   c. do not ask for
   d. plead

B. ➤ **Text Structure/Elements of Literature:** Read and choose the correct answer. *(28 points: 4 points each)*

┌───┐
"My Friend Mia"

1   Mia stood with her arms crossed while I tried to explain. "I'm sorry I was so late," I said. "My dad's car wouldn't start." But Mia did not feel forgiving. She yelled, "Rosa, you do this all the time! I really wanted to see that movie, but now it's too late." Then she turned and walked away, leaving me to wonder if we'd ever be friends again.
└───┘

7. Who is the narrator of "My Friend Mia"?
   a. Rosa
   b. Mia
   c. Rosa's dad
   d. someone outside the story

8. Authors use ____ when the narrator is a character in a story.
   a. the passive voice
   b. sequence of events
   c. fiction
   d. first-person point of view

9. "My Friend Mia" uses informal language. This is an example of ____.
   a. mood
   b. style
   c. imagery
   d. a conclusion

10. In "My Friend Mia," what is the mood of the last sentence?
    a. excitement
    b. happiness
    c. worry
    d. peacefulness

91

QUIZ Unit 6 • Chapter 2 (continued)

11. What is the conflict in "My Friend Mia"?
   a. Rosa's dad has problems with his car.
   b. Mia is angry because Rosa is late again.
   c. Mia and Rosa want to see different movies.
   d. Rosa is angry because Mia is late again.

12. Tone is _____.
   a. how the author feels about story characters and events
   b. how the reader feels about story events
   c. wanting to know what happens next
   d. the names and actions of story characters

13. _____ is the events that make up a fiction story.
   a. Dialogue
   b. Homophones
   c. Facts
   d. Plot

C. ➤ Reading Strategies: Choose the correct answer. (16 points: 4 points each)

14. The most important idea in a paragraph is the _____.
   a. main idea
   b. inference
   c. future tense
   d. point of view

15. Details are _____.
   a. guesses about what will happen next in a story
   b. where and when a story happens
   c. examples that help you understand the main idea
   d. words that compare two different nouns

16. Mia and Rosa argue a lot. Which detail supports this main idea?
   a. They like to eat ice cream together.
   b. They sometimes study at Rosa's house.
   c. Rosa was born in July.
   d. Rosa got mad at Mia for not calling.

17. Children learn languages more easily than adults. Which main idea does this detail support?
   a. Children are great learners.
   b. Children are very cute.
   c. Many children like animals.
   d. Most children like playing outside.

D. ➤ Grammar/Usage: Choose the correct answer. (12 points: 4 points each)

18. The _____ shows that a past action happened before another action.
   a. present participle
   b. future continuous tense
   c. present tense
   d. past perfect tense

19. I _____ the book before him.
   a. has finished
   b. had finished
   c. will finish
   d. am finishing

20. Bea _____ the whole house before Joe arrived to help.
   a. will paint
   b. is painting
   c. had painted
   d. has painted

E. ➤ Writing (20 points)

Writing Prompt Write a fictional story about finding a special object. Describe where you found the object, what you think it is used for, and how you will use it.

QUIZ Unit 6 • Chapter 3

A. ➤ Vocabulary: Choose the correct answer. *(28 points: 4 points each)*

1. A _____ is a part of a word.
   a. syllable
   b. preposition
   c. summary
   d. verb

   > **mis·chie·vous** /ˈmɪstʃəvəs/ *adjective*
   > **1** playfully annoying **2** causing harm or annoyance

2. In this dictionary entry, how many syllables does <u>mischievous</u> have?
   a. 1
   b. 2
   c. 3
   d. 4

3. Which sentence uses *mischievous* correctly?
   a. The girl was mischievous so she spelled the word correctly.
   b. Adi is mischievous; he plays tricks on me all the time.
   c. Mr. Martinez has a nice, mischievous house.
   d. Your big brother won the mischievous race.

4. When *-ian* is added to a word, it is a _____.
   a. prefix
   b. homophone
   c. suffix
   d. preposition

5. A person who works in a library is called a _____.
   a. librarian
   b. bookkeeper
   c. writer
   d. mathematician

6. A person who works with comedy is called a(n) _____.
   a. pediatrician
   b. comedian
   c. agrarian
   d. Bostonian

7. Which word has the root word <u>music</u>?
   a. museum
   b. mathematician
   c. librarian
   d. musician

B. ➤ Text Structure/Elements of Literature: Read and choose the correct answer. *(20 points: 4 points each)*

> "Gandhi: A Man for Peace"
>
> 1   Born in 1869, Mohandas Gandhi was a leader in India. He used nonviolent ways to end British rule of his country. Gandhi felt that armed conflict would hurt India. Instead, he asked the Indian people to stop buying British goods and to stop obeying unfair British laws. In 1947, India won independence. But Gandhi, the man who was against violence, was shot a year later.

8. The purpose of "Gandhi: A Man for Peace" is to describe _____.
   a. the food of India
   b. what Gandhi looked like
   c. events in Gandhi's life
   d. life in India today

9. What happened in 1948?
   a. Gandhi was shot.
   b. India became independent.
   c. Gandhi was born.
   d. Gandhi returned to India.

QUIZ Unit 6 • Chapter 3 (continued)

10. A _____ is an important topic in a reading.
    a. root word
    b. theme
    c. conclusion
    d. paraphrase

11. One theme of "Gandhi: A Man for Peace" is _____.
    a. peace and nonviolence are powerful tools
    b. children can help their communities
    c. a good education is important
    d. all countries use war to win independence

12. A biography _____.
    a. tells the events of a person's life
    b. tells the events of the author's life
    c. is a made-up story
    d. always uses rhyme

C. ➤ **Reading Strategies:** Choose the correct answer. *(16 points: 4 points each)*

13. A cause is _____.
    a. how a word is pronounced
    b. when an event happens
    c. a statement that supports a main idea
    d. the reason an event happens

14. An effect is _____.
    a. a tool for finding definitions
    b. what happens as a result of a cause
    c. a summary of the most important ideas in a text
    d. a word that takes the place of a noun

15. Effect: My kitchen is clean. What is the most likely cause?
    a. I mopped the floor and did the dishes.
    b. I cooked my father breakfast.
    c. I came home late from school.
    d. I opened the window to let in the fresh air.

16. Cause: I forgot to call home. What is the most likely effect?
    a. I lost my wallet.
    b. My parents were worried.
    c. I played football with friends.
    d. It started to snow.

D. ➤ **Grammar/Usage:** Choose the correct answer. (16 points: 4 points each)

17. I would have gone with you if you had asked me. Which word is the modal auxiliary?
    a. would
    b. gone
    c. with
    d. asked

18. He might have played soccer when he was young. Which word is the modal auxiliary?
    a. might
    b. played
    c. when
    d. was

19. If he knew, he _____ have told me.
    a. was
    b. had
    c. would
    d. not

20. Enrico _____ have liked the story.
    a. might
    b. did
    c. were
    d. is

E. ➤ **Writing** (20 points)

> **Writing Prompt** Write a biography about one of your family members. Include any interesting events and important dates in this person's life.

Grade

QUIZ Unit 6 • Chapter 4

A. ➤ Vocabulary: Choose the correct answer. *(20 points: 4 points each)*

1. Which is a connotative definition?
   a. raisin: a dried grape
   b. breeze: a light wind
   c. opening: a hole in something
   d. noon: twelve o'clock

2. Which is a denotative definition?
   a. fume: a bad gas or smell
   b. slam: to shut something angrily
   c. breath: air moved in and out of the lungs
   d. gadget: an inexpensive and unnecessary tool

3. Marta walks every day. She _____ walks.
   a. never   c. seldom
   b. rarely   d. always

4. Most of the time, the weather is nice. The weather is _____ nice.
   a. often   c. seldom
   b. never   d. always

5. Which sentence is correct?
   a. I miss you, I often see you.
   b. Juan's house is a mess because he always cleans it.
   c. I usually wake up early, but I sometimes sleep late.
   d. You like cheese very much so you rarely eat it.

B. ➤ Text Structure/Elements of Literature: Read and choose the correct answer. *(32 points: 4 points each)*

"The Language Family Tree"

1   Did you know that English and German are related? Most linguists (scientists who study language) agree that English and German are part of a language family called Germanic. A language family is a group of languages that shares similar traits like words and grammar.

6. "The Language Family Tree" is a(n) _____.
   a. informational text
   b. autobiography
   c. science fiction novel
   d. historical narrative

7. The subject of this reading is _____.
   a. how to speak German
   b. where English is spoken in the world
   c. that English and German are related
   d. how to become a linguist

8. Which is a graphic feature that would help you understand this reading?
   a. a list of synonyms for the word linguist
   b. a drawing of a language family tree
   c. a summary of the paragraph
   d. an article about German culture

9. English and German are related languages. Which sentence supports this important idea?
   a. People speak German in Germany.
   b. English and German have similar words.
   c. Germanic is an old language family.
   d. Linguists study languages.

"Esperanto!"

1   *Saluton!* This means "hello" in Esperanto, one of the world's few invented languages. Esperanto was invented in the late 1800s by L. L. Zamenhof. He believed that it would help people communicate. Even though Esperanto did not become a universal language, some people still speak it today.

10. Why did Zamenhof invent Esperanto?
    a. to help people communicate
    b. he liked the way it sounded
    c. he thought it would be easy to learn
    d. to end war

QUIZ Unit 6 • Chapter 4 (continued)

11. Both "The Language Family Tree" and "Esperanto!" discuss _____.
   a. German
   b. L. L. Zamenhof
   c. Esperanto
   d. language

12. L. L. Zamenhof was probably a(n) ___.
   a. police officer
   b. actor
   c. linguist
   d. dancer

13. Esperanto is one of the only invented languages. Which detail supports this fact?
   a. Few people learned Esperanto.
   b. Esperanto was created to help people communicate.
   c. *Saluton* means "hello" in Esperanto.
   d. Some people still speak Esperanto.

C. ➤ **Reading Strategies:** Choose the correct answer. *(12 points: 4 points each)*

14. When you paraphrase, you _____.
   a. decide if something is a fact
   b. use your own words to say or write what you read
   c. draw pictures to describe images
   d. write the important ideas in a text

15. Clara did many things today. Which sentence paraphrases this sentence?
   a. Clara had a great time today.
   b. Clara was busy today.
   c. Clara was not busy today.
   d. Clara had a bad day.

16. My friend, Jane, adores parrots. Which is a paraphrase of this sentence?
   a. Parrots are the best birds.
   b. Jane is an animal-lover.
   c. My friend, Jane, adores parrots.
   d. Jane really likes parrots.

D. ➤ **Grammar/Usage:** Choose the correct answer. *(16 points: 4 points each)*

17. _____ tell how often an action happens.
   a. Adverbs of frequency
   b. Passive voice sentences
   c. Metaphors and similes
   d. Dependent clauses

18. Which is an adverb of frequency?
   a. the
   b. slowly
   c. sometimes
   d. ate

19. Mia swims everyday. She _____ swims.
   a. seldom
   b. rarely
   c. never
   d. often

20. Jon is a vegetarian. He _____ eats meat.
   a. always
   b. never
   c. seldom
   d. sometimes

E. ➤ **Writing** *(20 points)*

> **Writing Prompt** Write an informational text explaining a topic you learned about in school.

TEST • Unit 6

A. ➤ Reading

Leaving Home

My Notes

1   She wasn't sure where she was going. She left the farmhouse and just started walking. Before long, she found herself on her special hill. This was where she always came when she wanted to be by herself.

2   She chose to sit under the maple tree. She liked the way it stood at the edge of the woods, yet leaned toward the open field below. She closed her eyes and leaned back against the tree.

3   Her parents sold the farm. Soon strangers would be living there and she would never again be part of its life.

4   What would living in the city be like? She would have to leave the large animals behind—the cows, pigs, and horses. Ranger was her horse, though not for much longer. She hoped that her friend Marco would be able to buy him.

5   At least the smaller animals would come with them. Her dog, Tally, and her cat, Simpson, would have to get used to city life. She would have to get used to it as well. Again, she wondered what it would be like. Would there be a friendly maple tree to lean against?

6   When she opened her eyes, she found that she could see the wind passing. The grasses of the field rippled like waves. Clouds raced across the sky. They soon caught and covered the sun.

7   Lightning flashed and thunder rumbled in the distance. The wind blew hard, laying the long grasses flat. A drop of rain splashed on her forehead as a warning. Then, the rain came in large, heavy drops, and the thunder and lightning got closer and more frequent. She got to her feet and turned back toward the woods, running for the umbrella of the trees. Now she understood that she had come to the hill to say goodbye.

TEST • Unit 6 *(continued)*

B. ➤ **Reading Comprehension:** Choose the correct answer. *(20 points: 2 points each)*

1. How will the city be different from the farm?
   a. There are no trees.
   b. Small animals cannot live there.
   c. There are no rainstorms.
   d. Large animals cannot live there.

2. What happened after the clouds covered the sun?
   a. The wind blew hard.
   b. The rain began to fall.
   c. Lightning flashed across the sky.
   d. The grass lay flat.

3. Why did the author write "Leaving Home"?
   a. to describe what a farm looks like
   b. to persuade the reader to find a special place
   c. to offer information about a farm
   d. to entertain the reader

4. What is the purpose of paragraphs 6 and 7?
   a. to describe what the girl sees
   b. to show the girl loved her home
   c. to prove to the reader the farm is beautiful
   d. to inform the reader about the storm

5. What does the sentence "Lightning flashed and thunder rumbled in the distance." make you picture in your mind?
   a. a gentle wind
   b. a calm rain
   c. a quiet shower
   d. a violent storm

6. What is the problem in "Leaving Home"?
   a. A terrible storm arrives.
   b. The girl can't find her way home.
   c. The girl is moving.
   d. The maple tree is gone.

7. "Leaving Home" is told from a _____.
   a. first-person point of view
   b. second-person point of view
   c. third-person point of view
   d. dramatic point of view

8. What does the girl like about the farm?
   a. the large animals
   b. the clouds
   c. the buildings
   d. the trains

9. Where does "Leaving Home" take place?
   a. in a barn
   b. in a suburb
   c. in the country
   d. in the city

10. Who is Ranger?
    a. the girl's cat
    b. the girl's pig
    c. the girl's horse
    d. the girl's dog

TEST • Unit 6 (continued)

C. ➤ Reading Strategies: Choose the correct answer. *(10 points: 2 points each)*

11. Why did the girl go to her special hill?
    a. She wanted to feel the rain.
    b. She wanted to see the clouds.
    c. She wanted to be alone.
    d. She wanted to visit a friend.

12. How did the girl feel about moving?
    a. excited
    b. nervous
    c. angry
    d. happy

13. What is the main idea of paragraph 2?
    a. The maple tree leaned toward the field.
    b. The girl leaned against the maple tree.
    c. The girl loves the maple tree.
    d. The maple tree is in the woods.

14. Summarize paragraph 3.
    a. The girl's parents sold their farm.
    b. The girl saw the river and valley.
    c. A stranger lived in the girl's house.
    d. The girl opened her eyes.

15. The picture of the girl helps you _____.
    a. understand the text
    b. identify the main idea
    c. understand suspense
    d. identify cause and effect

D. ➤ Elements of Literature: Choose the correct answer. *(10 points: 2 points each)*

16. "Leaving Home" is _____.
    a. fiction
    b. a biography
    c. nonfiction
    d. a play

17. How would "Leaving Home" be different if it were told from the girl's point of view?
    a. The reader would learn about more characters.
    b. The reader would better understand the feelings and thoughts of the girl.
    c. The reader would know the differences between a city and a farm.
    d. The reader would learn about taking care of a pet.

18. Which of the following best describes the overall mood in "Leaving Home"?
    a. excited
    b. humorous
    c. happy
    d. sad

19. What is the theme in "Leaving Home"?
    a. Moving to a new home can be difficult and sad.
    b. People don't have many pets in the city.
    c. A rainstorm is a relaxing experience.
    d. The farm is a beautiful place to live.

20. What does the girl realize at the end of "Leaving Home"?
    a. She will miss her home.
    b. She wants to move away.
    c. She came to the hill to say goodbye.
    d. She loves to be outside in the rain.

TEST • Unit 6 (continued)

E. ➤ **Vocabulary:** Read and choose the correct answer. *(10 points: 2 points each)*

> **warn-ing** /'wɔrnɪŋ/ *n.* [Old English] **1** danger sign, (*syn.*) an omen: *The pain in his chest was a warning about a possible heart attack.* **2** a statement that something bad might happen. (*syn.*) a caution: *The boss gave his workers a warning about being late.*

21. Look at the dictionary entry for the word warning. How many syllables does warning have?
    a. 1
    b. 2
    c. 3
    d. 4

22. What is a synonym for warning?
    a. caution
    b. memory
    c. help
    d. sign

23. From the context of paragraph 6, you know that the word rippled means _____.
    a. flowed
    b. hunted
    c. protected
    d. yelled

24. She was not sure where she was going. She felt _____.
    a. guilty
    b. confused
    c. confident
    d. joyful

25. From the context of paragraph 3, you know that the word stranger means _____.
    a. a person you don't know
    b. friends
    c. an animal
    d. a family name

F. ➤ **Grammar/Usage:** Choose the correct answer. *(10 points: 2 points each)*

26. Which sentence is correct?
    a. Matthew gave her a gift.
    b. Matthew gave his a gift.
    c. Matthew gave she a gift.
    d. Matthew gave I a gift.

27. Which sentence is correct?
    a. Karen moved to the city she visit last year.
    b. Karen moved to the city she visits last year.
    c. Karen moved to the city she had visited last year.
    d. Karen moved to the city she was visit last year.

28. Which sentence is correct?
    a. They are going to the zoo, but it was too cold.
    b. They would have gone to the zoo, but it was too cold.
    c. They go to the zoo, but it was too cold.
    d. They gone to the zoo, but it was too cold.

29. I exercise every day. In other words, I _____ exercise.
    a. often
    b. sometimes
    c. rarely
    d. never

30. Which sentence is correct?
    a. Judy came over to I house to study.
    b. Judy came over to we house to study.
    c. Judy came over to they house to study.
    d. Judy came over to my house to study.

TEST • Unit 6 *(continued)*

G. ➤ **Writing Conventions:** Choose the correct answer. *(10 points: 2 points each)*

31. Which word is spelled correctly?
   a. beld
   b. build
   c. bild
   d. biuld

32. Which is the abbreviation for <u>number</u>?
   a. nr.
   b. nu.
   c. no.
   d. nb.

33. Which of the following should be capitalized?
   a. park
   b. denton park
   c. city
   d. big city

34. Which of the following should be hyphenated?
   a. two horse
   b. dog house
   c. book case
   d. butter fly

35. Which word is spelled correctly?
   a. choces
   b. chioces
   c. choyces
   d. choices

H. ➤ **Editing:** Choose the correct answer. *(10 points: 2 points each)*

Dear Sam,

   (1) Thanks for coming to my birthday party. (2) I am really glad you are able to come help celebrate with me. (3) I really love the toy robot you have gave me for a present. (4) Maybe you could come over and play with them. (5) I hope you had the bestest time ever at my birthday party. (6) I can't wait until your birthday!

(7) Thanks,

Joanie

36. In sentence 1, the possessive adjective is ____.
   a. for
   b. party
   c. my
   d. thanks

37. What change should you make to sentence 2?
   a. add a comma between *really* and *glad*
   b. change *are able* to *were able*
   c. change *me* to *I*
   d. make no change

38. What change should you make to sentence 3?
   a. change *toy robot* to *toy-robot*
   b. change *robot* to *Robot*
   c. change *have gave* to *gave*
   d. make no change

39. What change should you make to sentence 4?
   a. change *Maybe* to *Might be*
   b. change *and* to *but*
   c. change *them* to *it*
   d. make no change

TEST • Unit 6 (continued)

40. What change should you make to sentence 5?
   a. change *had* to *has*
   b. change *bestest* to *best*
   c. change *birthday* to *Birthday*
   d. make no change

I. ➤ **Writing** (20 points)

> **Writing Prompt** Choose a special place that you like to visit. Write a fictional story in which a character visits that place. Describe what happens to the character. Use the Planning Guide to help you write.

Planning Guide
❑ Choose a setting and a main character.
❑ List details about the setting and the character.
❑ List important events that will happen in the story.
❑ Think about what the character will learn as a result of the trip to the special place.
❑ Check your writing for spelling, punctuation, and capitalization.

END-OF-BOOK EXAM

A. ➤ Reading

Waiting

1   Sergei's eyes popped open. He grabbed the clock. It was still early, but Mrs. Soo might call any minute.

My Notes

2   Sergei ate breakfast sitting next to the telephone. That way he could answer it quickly. He even picked up the phone to see if it was working.

3   Was that a knock? He put the phone down and raced to the door. There was no one there. Across the street, Elana was up, too, waiting for the same call. He went back inside and shut the door.

4   An hour went by, and Sergei's heart sank to the bottom of his shoes. He knew he wouldn't hear from Mrs. Soo because he had not made the team.

5   Then, he really did hear a knock. It was Elana, and she was grinning. Instead of saying anything, she just handed him a note. "I found it under the mat."

6   "Congratulations, Sergei. You will be our catcher. I tried calling, but your line was busy." Then Sergei remembered that he had never hung up the phone!

Twice as Much Fun

1   Dear Parents:

2   If you would like your son or daughter to be on a baseball team, please read the enclosed guidelines carefully. Make sure your child understands these safety rules. Then sign the permission slip and return it to the office.

3   Sincerely,

4   Edward Ramos, Principal

5   Dear Mr. Ramos,

6   Before I sign the permission slip, I would like to know more about the school rules. Can boys and girls play on the same team?

7   My children are twins, one boy and one girl. They are both good players and they want to be on the same team.

8   Sincerely,

9   Kim Lo

10 Dear Mrs. Lo:

11 Yes, girls and boys play on the same team. Not only that, but there might be three pairs of twins on their team! It should be quite a year.

12 Sincerely,

13 Edward Ramos, Principal

END-OF-BOOK EXAM *(continued)*

B. ➤ **Reading Comprehension:** Read and choose the correct answer.
(20 points: 2 points each)

Example: Who is the principal of the school?
a. Kim Lo
b. Sergei
c. Mrs. Soo
(d.) Edward Ramos

1. At the beginning of "Waiting," Sergei _____.
   a. just woke up
   b. is tired because he stayed up all night
   c. has just gotten home
   d. is eating dinner

2. In "Waiting," who gives Sergei the note?
   a. his mother
   b. Mrs. Soo
   c. Elana
   d. his teacher

3. In "Twice as Much Fun," what does Mr. Ramos ask parents to do after they sign the permission slip?
   a. make sure their children understand the safety rules
   b. send him letters with their questions
   c. buy baseball uniforms for their children
   d. send the permission slip to the school office

4. The picture helps you understand that Sergei _____.
   a. needs new sneakers
   b. will visit his grandmother
   c. wants to play baseball
   d. will go to the library to study

5. Who is Kim Lo in "Twice as Much Fun"?
   a. the principal of King Middle School
   b. a student at King Middle School
   c. the parent of students at King Middle School
   d. the baseball coach at King Middle School

6. In "Waiting," Sergei forgets to hang up the phone. This tells you that he is _____.
   a. worried and distracted
   b. relaxed and calm
   c. angry and upset
   d. happy and laughing

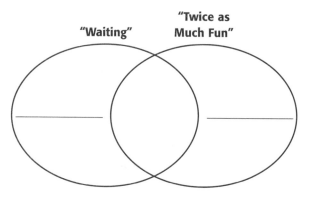

7. Complete the Venn Diagram. How are "Waiting" and "Twice as Much Fun" different?
   a. "Waiting" is science fiction; "Twice as Much Fun" is a poem.
   b. "Waiting" is fiction; "Twice as Much Fun" includes letters.
   c. "Waiting" is an informational text; "Twice as Much Fun" is a myth.
   d. "Waiting" is a biography; "Twice as Much Fun" is a speech.

8. From paragraph 5 of "Waiting," we know that Elana _____.
   a. is happy the Sergei makes the team
   b. is upset that Sergei makes the team
   c. doesn't like baseball
   d. talks on the phone often

9. What is the problem in "Twice as Much Fun"?
   a. The twins do not make the baseball team.
   b. A mother worries that her twins cannot be on the same team.
   c. The principal wants to end baseball at King Middle School.
   d. The twins want to be on different baseball teams.

END-OF-BOOK EXAM (continued)

10. In "Waiting," the note says that _____.
    a. Sergei should not play baseball
    b. Sergei should hang up his phone
    c. Sergei will be a member of the team
    d. Sergei should choose another sport to play

C. ➤ Reading Strategies: Read and choose the correct answer. *(10 points: 2 points each)*

11. From paragraph 3 of "Waiting," you can infer that Elana _____.
    a. goes to school with Sergei
    b. is Sergei's cousin
    c. also wants to be on the team
    d. likes baseball better than tennis

12. Both "Waiting" and "Twice as Much Fun" are about _____.
    a. twins
    b. sports
    c. school
    d. telephones

13. In "Twice as Much Fun," what causes Kim Lo to send the letter?
    a. She wants to know if her twins can play on the same team.
    b. She needs to introduce herself to Principal Ramos.
    c. She must set up a meeting with Principal Ramos.
    d. She wants to learn what her twins are studying in class.

14. Which sentence best summarizes "Waiting"?
    a. Elana does not sleep all night because she is worried about Sergei.
    b. Elana and Sergei have a fight about whether they made the team.
    c. Sergei nervously waits to learn that he made the team.
    d. Sergei learns that he made the team, but he does not care.

15. Which sentence from "Twice as Much Fun" is an opinion?
    a. Yes, girls and boys play on the same team.
    b. Make sure your child understands these safety rules.
    c. My children are twins, one boy and one girl.
    d. It should be quite a year.

D. ➤ Elements of Literature: Read and choose the correct answer. *(10 points: 2 points each)*

16. The main character in "Waiting" is _____.
    a. Mrs. Soo
    b. Sergei
    c. Elana
    d. the team

17. Sergei's heart sank to the bottom of his shoes. This sentence means Sergei _____.
    a. felt very upset
    b. became very happy
    c. went to the bottom of the ocean
    d. ruined his shoes

18. From Kim Lo's letter in "Twice as Much Fun," you can infer that she _____.
    a. does not like school
    b. does not like sports
    c. cares a lot about her children
    d. is happy with the school

19. Which sentence contrasts the moods of the two readings?
    a. "Waiting" is suspenseful, and "Twice as Much Fun" is friendly.
    b. "Waiting" is happy, and "Twice as Much Fun" is angry.
    c. "Waiting" is calm, and "Twice as Much Fun" is scary.
    d. "Waiting" is angry, and "Twice as Much Fun" is exciting.

END-OF-BOOK EXAM (continued)

20. What theme do both readings share?
  a. Some sports are more interesting than others.
  b. Boys and girls should play on different sports teams.
  c. Only girls should play sports.
  d. Sports are important to many people.

E. ➤ Vocabulary: Choose the correct answer. *(10 points: 2 points each)*

21. From paragraph 2 of "Twice as Much Fun," you know that a <u>permission slip</u> is a ____.
  a. shoe worn by softball players
  b. paper allowing someone to do something
  c. a note to students
  d. type of baseball equipment

22. From paragraph 6 of "Waiting," you can guess that the word <u>catcher</u> means a ____.
  a. person who opens doors for others
  b. person in baseball who throws balls
  c. person in baseball who catches balls
  d. person who hits the ball

Word:	Sentence:
twins	Anthony and Gary are twins; people have a hard time telling them apart.
Meaning:	Symbol:

23. Use paragraphs 7 and 11 of "Twice as Much Fun" to complete the word square. <u>Twins</u> means ____.
  a. an older brother and a younger sister
  b. friends who like to do everything together
  c. family members who are related to the father
  d. two children born from the same mother at the same time

popped /pɑpt'/ *v.* **1** made a loud sound **2** burst open quickly **3** ate suddenly **4** left quickly

24. Read this dictionary entry for the word <u>popped</u>. Which meaning most closely matches the meaning of <u>popped</u> in paragraph 1 of "Waiting"?
  a. definition 1
  b. definition 2
  c. definition 3
  d. definition 4

25. What is the connotative meaning of the word <u>raced</u> from paragraph 3 of "Waiting"?
  a. moved quickly with a feeling of anxiety
  b. moved slowly with a feeling of sadness
  c. moved quickly with a feeling of fear
  d. moved slowly with a feeling of boredom

END-OF-BOOK EXAM (continued)

F. ➤ **Grammar/Usage:** Choose the correct answer. *(10 points: 2 points each)*

26. Which sentence is correct?
   a. Ariela were at my house last night.
   b. Ariela is at my house last night.
   c. Ariela was at my house last night.
   d. Ariela be at my house last night.

27. Which sentence is a command?
   a. The people are happy.
   b. Let the people be happy.
   c. The people should be happy.
   d. All people want to be happy.

28. Juanita is the _____ swimmer on the team.
   a. stronger
   b. strong
   c. strongly
   d. strongest

29. Which sentence contains a prepositional phrase?
   a. Jahlil is learning to fix cars.
   b. Kayla is sad because she cannot go.
   c. Carmen lives with her dad in Chicago.
   d. They painted their house yellow.

30. Yesterday, she _____ breakfast before I got up.
   a. had eaten
   b. have eaten
   c. eaten
   d. eats

G. ➤ **Writing Conventions:** Choose the correct answer. *(10 points: 2 points each)*

31. Which sentence is correct?
   a. Texas' climate can be warm.
   b. Texas climate can be warm.
   c. Texas's climate can be warm.
   d. Texa's climate can be warm.

32. The nicest park in New York City is _____.
   a. central park
   b. Central park
   c. central Park
   d. Central Park

33. Which sentence correctly abbreviates the temperature Celsius?
   a. It is 20°C.
   b. It is 20C°.
   c. It is 20 degrees Cel.
   d. It is 20 Cel degrees.

34. The number 36 is written as _____.
   a. thirty six
   b. thirty-six
   c. thirtysix
   d. thirty six-

35. We _____ the answer.
   a. now
   b. no
   c. know
   d. kno

END-OF-BOOK EXAM (continued)

H. ➤ Editing: Read and choose the correct answer. *(10 points: 2 points each)*

"My Father"

(1) My father was born on 1955 in New Mexico. (2) Her father was a Ute Indian who raised sheep and cattle. (3) Today, my father writes poems about his childhood. (4) Life was very tough for the family. (5) There was always enough money to buy things they needed, so they wore their clothing until it ripped or was too small. (6) When my father was 10, his family moves to California.

---

36. What change should you make to sentence 1?
    a. change *My* to *Mine*
    b. change *born* to *bored*
    c. change *on* to *in*
    d. make no change

37. What change should you make to sentence 2?
    a. change *Her* to *My*
    b. change *Ute Indian* to *ute indian*
    c. change *raised* to *raise*
    d. make no change

38. For a better sequence of events, sentence 3 should _____.
    a. move after sentence 5
    b. move to the beginning of the paragraph
    c. move to the end of the paragraph
    d. stay where it is

39. What change should you make to sentence 5?
    a. change *always* to *seldom*
    b. change *always* to *sometimes*
    c. change *their* to *they*
    d. change *ripped* to *riped*

40. What change should you make to sentence 6?
    a. change *When* to *Where*
    b. change *his* to *her*
    c. change *moves* to *moved*
    d. make no change

I. ➤ Writing *(20 points)*

Writing Prompt Write a three-paragraph personal narrative about a time when you learned something new. Use the Planning Guide to help you write.

Planning Guide
❑ Answer these questions before you write:
  a. When did you learn something new?
  b. What did you learn?
  c. Where did you learn it? Did someone teach it to you? Who?
  d. How did you feel about learning it? Excited? Interested? Why?
❑ Use first-person pronouns (*I, me, we,* and *us*).
❑ Remember to indent each paragraph.
❑ Include an introduction and a conclusion.
❑ Check your writing for spelling, capitalization, and punctuation.

Answer Key

Diagnostic Test

A. Vocabulary Meaning
1. c   3. d   5. a
2. c   4. a

B. Word Study
6. c   8. b   10. b
7. d   9. c

C. Reading Comprehension
Reading 1
11. c   13. a   15. c
12. b   14. b
Reading 2
16. c   18. b   20. b
17. c   19. a

D. Reading Strategies
21. a   23. a   25. b
22. c   24. c

E. Grammar/Usage
26. d   28. c   30. b
27. c   29. c

F. Spelling
31. c   33. d   35. d
32. c   34. c

G. Writing
Answers will vary.

H. Writing Conventions
36. a   38. b   40. b
37. b   39. b

Unit 1
Chapter 1 Quiz

A. Vocabulary
1. b   4. a   7. b
2. b   5. d   8. c
3. c   6. a

B. Text Structure/Elements of Literature
9. c   11. d
10. a   12. b

C. Reading Strategies
13. d   14. c   15. d

D. Grammar/Usage
16. c   18. b   20. d
17. c   19. d

E. Writing
Answers will vary.

Unit 1
Chapter 2 Quiz

A. Vocabulary
1. b   4. a   7. c
2. d   5. d   8. c
3. b   6. b

B. Text Structure/Elements of Literature
9. c   10. a   11. a

C. Reading Strategies
12. d   13. b   14. b

D. Grammar/Usage
15. a   17. b   19. c
16. b   18. a   20. b

E. Writing
Answers will vary.

Unit 1
Chapter 3 Quiz

A. Vocabulary
1. b   4. b   7. d
2. c   5. c
3. a   6. a

B. Text Structure/Elements of Literature
8. d   10. b
9. a   11. d

C. Reading Strategies
12. d   13. b   14. c

D. Grammar/Usage
15. c   17. d   19. a
16. b   18. a   20. a

E. Writing
Answers will vary.

Unit 1
Chapter 4 Quiz

A. Vocabulary
1. b   4. d   7. c
2. b   5. d   8. a
3. d   6. b

B. Text Structure/Elements of Literature
9. c   11. b
10. a   12. d

C. Reading Strategies
13. a   14. c   15. b

D. Grammar/Usage
16. d   18. b   20. d
17. d   19. b

E. Writing
Answers will vary.

Unit 1
Chapter 5 Quiz

A. Vocabulary
1. c   3. b   5. a
2. d   4. d   6. d

B. Text Structure/Elements of Literature
7. c   9. a   11. c
8. d   10. a   12. d

C. Reading Strategies
13. a   15. a
14. d   16. c

D. Grammar/Usage
17. a   19. b
18. a   20. a

E. Writing
Answers will vary.

Unit 1 Test

B. Reading Comprehension
1. b   5. d   9. b
2. c   6. a   10. d
3. a   7. b
4. c   8. c

C. Reading Strategies
11. b   13. c   15. b
12. a   14. d

D. Elements of Literature
16. d   18. a   20. a
17. a   19. c

E. Vocabulary
21. d   23. a   25. c
22. b   24. b

F. Grammar/Usage
26. a   28. a   30. c
27. c   29. d

G. Writing Conventions
31. a   33. a   35. a
32. c   34. d

H. Editing
36. b   38. a   40. b
37. c   39. c

I. Writing
Answers will vary.

Unit 2
Chapter 1 Quiz

A. Vocabulary
1. b   3. a   5. c
2. c   4. d   6. b

B. Text Structure/Elements of Literature
7. a   10. b   13. b
8. d   11. d   14. b
9. a   12. d

C. Reading Strategies
15. c   16. a   17. d

D. Grammar/Usage
18. b   19. d   20. a

E. Writing
Answers will vary.

Unit 2
Chapter 2 Quiz

A. Vocabulary
1. c   3. a   5. b
2. c   4. c   6. c

B. Text Structure/Elements of Literature
7. b   10. a   13. d
8. d   11. b   14. a
9. c   12. d

C. Reading Strategies
15. b   16. a   17. c

D. Grammar/Usage
18. b   19. d   20. a

E. Writing
Answers will vary.

Unit 2
Chapter 3 Quiz

A. Vocabulary
1. b   3. c   5. b
2. a   4. d   6. a

B. Text Structure/Elements of Literature
7. c   10. c   13. b
8. a   11. d   14. c
9. d   12. a

C. Reading Strategies
15. c   16. b   17. c

D. Grammar/Usage
18. a   19. d   20. b

E. Writing
Answers will vary.

Unit 2
Chapter 4 Quiz

A. Vocabulary
1. a   3. d   5. a
2. b   4. b   6. b

B. Text Structure/Elements of Literature
7. b   10. a   13. b
8. c   11. a   14. d
9. b   12. c

C. Reading Strategies
15. c   16. c   17. c

D. Grammar/Usage
18. a   19. c   20. b

E. Writing
Answers will vary.

Unit 2
Chapter 5 Quiz

A. Vocabulary
1. b   3. a   5. d
2. c   4. d   6. c

B. Text Structure/Elements of Literature
7. c   10. d   13. a
8. b   11. c   14. d
9. a   12. b

C. Reading Strategies
15. b   16. a   17. c

D. Grammar/Usage
18. b   19. d   20. b

E. Writing
Answers will vary.

Unit 2 Test

B. Reading Comprehension
1. b   5. a   9. b
2. a   6. b   10. a
3. c   7. a
4. d   8. d

C. Reading Strategies
11. b   13. d   15. b
12. c   14. a

D. Elements of Literature
16. c   18. a   20. a
17. b   19. d

E. Vocabulary
21. d   23. c   25. b
22. b   24. d

F. Grammar/Usage
26. d   28. a   30. c
27. b   29. b

G. Writing Conventions
31. d   33. c   35. d
32. c   34. b

H. Editing
36. a   38. c   40. c
37. a   39. d

I. Writing
Answers will vary.

Unit 3
Chapter 1 Quiz

A. Vocabulary
1. b   3. a   5. c
2. b   4. d   6. d

B. Text Structure/Elements of Literature
7. d   9. a   11. c
8. c   10. d   12. a

C. Reading Strategies
13. b   14. c   15. a

D. Grammar/Usage
16. d   18. b   20. c
17. c   19. a

E. Writing
Answers will vary.

Unit 3
Chapter 2 Quiz

A. Vocabulary
1. d   4. c   7. c
2. b   5. b
3. a   6. d

B. Text Structure/Elements of Literature
8. a   10. b   12. b
9. c   11. c   13. b

C. Reading Strategies
14. a   16. b
15. d   17. a

D. Grammar/Usage
18. c   19. d   20. b

E. Writing
Answers will vary.

Unit 3
Chapter 3 Quiz

A. Vocabulary
1. a   3. d   5. b
2. b   4. c   6. a

B. Text Structure/Elements of Literature
7. d   9. c
8. b   10. a

C. Reading Strategies
11. d   13. b   15. d
12. a   14. c

D. Grammar/Usage
16. c   18. a   20. d
17. a   19. b

E. Writing
Answers will vary.

Unit 3
Chapter 4 Quiz

A. Vocabulary
1. b   4. d   7. a
2. d   5. d
3. a   6. b

B. Text Structure/Elements of Literature
8. c   11. d   14. d
9. d   12. b
10. a   13. c

C. Reading Strategies
15. c   16. b   17. d

D. Grammar/Usage
18. a   19. b   20. d

E. Writing
Answers will vary.

Unit 3
Chapter 5 Quiz

A. Vocabulary
1. c   4. b   7. c
2. a   5. d
3. c   6. d

B. Text Structure/Elements of Literature
8. a   10. b
9. c   11. d

C. Reading Strategies
12. a   14. c
13. d   15. a

D. Grammar/Usage
16. a   18. b   20. c
17. a   19. b

E. Writing
Answers will vary.

Unit 3 Test

B. Reading Comprehension
1. a   5. c   9. a
2. b   6. a   10. a
3. d   7. c
4. b   8. b

C. Reading Strategies
11. c   13. a   15. a
12. d   14. d

D. Elements of Literature
16. a   18. a   20. b
17. c   19. c

E. Vocabulary
21. c   23. a   25. d
22. c   24. d

F. Grammar/Usage
26. a   28. b   30. a
27. b   29. c

G. Writing Conventions
31. c   33. b   35. a
32. a   34. c

H. Editing
36. c   38. b   40. a
37. c   39. c

I. Writing
Answers will vary.

Mid-Book Exam

B. Reading Comprehension
1. a   5. a   9. b
2. c   6. b   10. c
3. c   7. c
4. b   8. b

C. Reading Strategies
11. a   13. a   15. c
12. c   14. a

D. Elements of Literature
16. b   18. a   20. c
17. a   19. b

E. Vocabulary
21. b   23. a   25. d
22. a   24. c

F. Grammar/Usage
26. c   28. c   30. d
27. a   29. a

G. Writing Conventions
31. c   33. d   35. c
32. c   34. b

H. Editing
36. b   38. b   40. a
37. a   39. c

I. Writing
Answers will vary.

Unit 4
Chapter 1 Quiz

A. Vocabulary

1. d	3. c	5. a
2. a	4. b	

B. Text Structure/Elements of Literature

6. c	8. d	10. c
7. a	9. b	11. a

C. Reading Strategies

12. b	13. a	14. d

D. Grammar/Usage

15. c	17. b	19. b
16. a	18. d	20. c

E. Writing
Answers will vary.

Unit 4
Chapter 2 Quiz

A. Vocabulary

1. c	3. a	5. a
2. b	4. d	6. c

B. Text Structure/Elements of Literature

7. d	9. a	11. b
8. c	10. c	

C. Reading Strategies

12. a	14. a	16. b
13. d	15. c	

D. Grammar/Usage

17. d	19. a
18. c	20. b

E. Writing
Answers will vary.

Unit 4
Chapter 3 Quiz

A. Vocabulary

1. b	3. b	5. a
2. c	4. c	6. d

B. Text Structure/Elements of Literature

7. a	10. b	13. c
8. c	11. c	
9. a	12. d	

C. Reading Strategies

14. d	16. c
15. a	17. b

D. Grammar/Usage

18. a	19. b	20. a

E. Writing
Answers will vary.

Unit 4
Chapter 4 Quiz

A. Vocabulary

1. b	3. d	5. a
2. d	4. c	

B. Text Structure/Elements of Literature

6. b	8. a	10. a
7. c	9. b	11. b

C. Reading Strategies

12. d	14. b
13. c	15. a

D. Grammar/Usage

16. c	18. c	20. a
17. b	19. a	

E. Writing
Answers will vary.

Unit 4 Test

B. Reading Comprehension

1. b	5. d	9. c
2. a	6. b	10. b
3. c	7. a	
4. c	8. b	

C. Reading Strategies

11. b	13. d	15. c
12. d	14. b	

D. Elements of Literature

16. d	18. d	20. a
17. c	19. b	

E. Vocabulary

21. b	23. a	25. b
22. c	24. a	

F. Grammar/Usage

26. b	28. a	30. c
27. c	29. d	

G. Writing Conventions

31. b	33. d	35. c
32. c	34. c	

H. Editing

36. a	38. d	40. c
37. a	39. a	

I. Writing
Answers will vary.

Unit 5
Chapter 1 Quiz

A. Vocabulary

1. b	4. c	7. d
2. c	5. c	
3. a	6. b	

B. Text Structure/Elements of Literature

8. a	10. d	12. a
9. c	11. b	

C. Reading Strategies

13. d	14. c	15. b

D. Grammar/Usage

16. c	18. a	20. b
17. b	19. d	

E. Writing
Answers will vary.

Unit 5
Chapter 2 Quiz

A. Vocabulary

1. d	3. b	5. b
2. a	4. c	6. a

B. Text Structure/Elements of Literature

7. a	9. a
8. b	10. d

C. Reading Strategies

11.	d	13.	b
12.	c	14.	a

D. Grammar/Usage

15.	d	17.	c	19.	a
16.	a	18.	d	20.	b

E. Writing
Answers will vary.

Unit 5
Chapter 3 Quiz

A. Vocabulary

1.	b	3.	d	5.	a
2.	c	4.	a		

B. Text Structure/Elements of Literature

6.	b	9.	b	12.	c
7.	c	10.	d		
8.	a	11.	b		

C. Reading Strategies

13.	a	15.	d	17.	d
14.	c	16.	b		

D. Grammar/Usage

18.	a	19.	c	20.	b

E. Writing
Answers will vary.

Unit 5
Chapter 4 Quiz

A. Vocabulary

1.	b	3.	b	5.	c
2.	d	4.	a		

B. Text Structure/Elements of Literature

6.	a	8.	c	10.	b
7.	c	9.	d		

C. Reading Strategies

11.	d	13.	a
12.	b	14.	c

D. Grammar/Usage

15.	a	17.	b	19.	c
16.	d	18.	a	20.	b

E. Writing
Answers will vary.

Unit 5 Test

B. Reading Comprehension

1.	c	5.	d	9.	d
2.	d	6.	b	10.	a
3.	b	7.	c		
4.	b	8.	d		

C. Reading Strategies

11.	a	13.	b	15.	b
12.	b	14.	a		

D. Elements of Literature

16.	a	18.	a	20.	c
17.	b	19.	b		

E. Vocabulary

21.	a	23.	a	25.	b
22.	c	24.	c		

F. Grammar/Usage

26.	b	28.	c	30.	c
27.	d	29.	a		

G. Writing Conventions

31.	d	33.	d	35.	b
32.	d	34.	c		

H. Editing

36.	c	38.	a	40.	c
37.	d	39.	a		

I. Writing
Answers will vary.

Unit 6
Chapter 1 Quiz

A. Vocabulary

1.	a	4.	b	7.	c
2.	c	5.	b		
3.	a	6.	d		

B. Text Structure/Elements of Literature

8.	a	10.	b
9.	d	11.	a

C. Reading Strategies

12.	c	14.	b
13.	d	15.	a

D. Grammar/Usage

16.	d	18.	a	20.	c
17.	b	19.	c		

E. Writing
Answers will vary.

Unit 6
Chapter 2 Quiz

A. Vocabulary

1.	b	3.	a	5.	b
2.	d	4.	c	6.	d

B. Text Structure/Elements of Literature

7.	a	10.	c	13.	d
8.	d	11.	b		
9.	b	12.	a		

C. Reading Strategies

14.	a	16.	d
15.	c	17.	a

D. Grammar/Usage

18.	d	19.	b	20.	c

E. Writing
Answers will vary.

Unit 6
Chapter 3 Quiz

A. Vocabulary

1.	a	4.	c	7.	d
2.	c	5.	a		
3.	b	6.	b		

B. Text Structure/Elements of Literature

8.	c	10.	b	12.	a
9.	a	11.	a		

C. Reading Strategies

13.	d	15.	a
14.	b	16.	b

D. Grammar/Usage

17.	a	19.	c
18.	a	20.	a

E. Writing
Answers will vary.

Unit 6
Chapter 4 Quiz

A. Vocabulary

1.	b	3.	d	5.	c
2.	c	4.	a		

B. Text Structure/Elements of Literature

6. a	9. b	12. c
7. c	10. a	13. b
8. b	11. d	

C. Reading Strategies

14. b	15. b	16. d

D. Grammar/Usage

17. a	19. d
18. c	20. b

E. Writing
Answers will vary.

Unit 6 Test

B. Reading Comprehension

1. d	5. d	9. c
2. c	6. c	10. c
3. d	7. c	
4. a	8. a	

C. Reading Strategies

11. c	13. c	15. a
12. b	14. a	

D. Elements of Literature

16. a	18. d	20. c
17. b	19. a	

E. Vocabulary

21. b	23. a	25. a
22. a	24. b	

F. Grammar/Usage

26. a	28. b	30. d
27. c	29. a	

G. Writing Conventions

31. b	33. b	35. d
32. c	34. a	

H. Editing

36. c	38. c	40. b
37. b	39. c	

I. Writing
Answers will vary.

End-of-Book Exam

B. Reading Comprehension

1. a	5. c	9. b
2. c	6. a	10. c
3. d	7. b	
4. c	8. a	

C. Reading Strategies

11. c	13. a	15. d
12. b	14. c	

D. Elements of Literature

16. b	18. c	20. d
17. a	19. a	

E. Vocabulary

21. b	23. d	25. a
22. c	24. b	

F. Grammar/Usage

26. c	28. d	30. a
27. b	29. c	

G. Writing Conventions

31. c	33. a	35. c
32. d	34. b	

H. Editing

36. c	38. c	40. c
37. a	39. a	

I. Writing
Answers will vary.

📁 Portfolio: Activity Rating and Reflection Sheet

Part I: Rating

Write the name of each activity in your work folder on the left. Think about how much you liked it. Circle one number for each activity.

Unit ___ Activities	I didn't like it.	I liked it a little.	I liked it.	I liked it very much.
_____	1	2	3	4
_____	1	2	3	4
_____	1	2	3	4
_____	1	2	3	4
_____	1	2	3	4
_____	1	2	3	4
_____	1	2	3	4
_____	1	2	3	4

Part II: Reflection

1. **My Portfolio choice for Unit ____**

   I chose to put _____ in my Portfolio because

   _____ .

2. **How I Learned**

   I learned best from . . .

   ____ listening and speaking.   ____ reading.   ____ writing.

   I liked working . . .

   ____ by myself. ____ with a partner. ____ with a small group. ____ with the whole class.

VISIONS STUDENT RESOURCE

Reading Fluency Chart

How many words did you read in one minute? Color in the graph up to the number of words that you read.

When you read silently, color in the chart with red. When you read orally, color in the chart with blue.

Words per Minute	Key: Silent Reading = Red Oral Reading = Blue
180	
175	
170	
165	
160	
155	
150	
145	
140	
135	
130	
125	
120	
115	
110	
105	
100	
95	
90	
85	
80	
75	
70	
65	
60	
55	
50	
45	
40	
35	
30	
25	
20	
15	
10	

Reading Exercise	1	2	3	4	5	1	2	3	4	5	1	2	3	4	5	1	2	3	4	1	2	3	4	1	2	3	4
Unit		1					2					3					4				5				6		

Responding to Peers' Writing: *EQS*

E: Encourage	*Q*: Question	*S*: Suggestions
• Help your partner recognize what he or she is doing right. • Be specific. Say things like: "I liked the surprise at the end the best." "You used some very interesting words in this sentence." "This poem made me think of my home."	• Ask questions when you would like more information. • Ask questions when something isn't clear. For example: "Why did your grandmother give you that picture?" "What do you mean, 'He went back'? Where did he go?"	• Ask your partner if he or she would like some suggestions. If your partner says "yes," offer suggestions to make the writing better. • Always let your partner choose whether or not to use your ideas. • Don't tell your partner what to do. Instead, make suggestions like: "You might try saying, 'My dog is fat' another way. How about 'My dog looks like a sausage with four legs'?" "What if you changed these two sentences around?"

Read your partner's selection. Use *EQS* to fill in the boxes.

Name _____   Partner's Name _____

E: Encourage	*Q*: Question	*S*: Suggestions

Peer Editing Checklist

Use this checklist to edit your peer's writing.
You may also use it to check your own writing.

Writer's Name _____

Editor's Name _____

1. Is there a title? _____ Yes _____ No

2. Is the first sentence of each paragraph indented? _____ Yes _____ No

3. Does each sentence start with a capital letter? _____ Yes _____ No

4. Does each sentence end with a punctuation mark? _____ Yes _____ No

5. Does each name start with a capital letter? _____ Yes _____ No

6. Write one correct sentence from the paper.

_____

7. Write one sentence that has a mistake.

_____

8. Rewrite the sentence correctly.

_____

Use these editing symbols:

¶	Start a new paragraph.
∧	Insert a word or words.
Sp	Correct a spelling error.
CAP	Use a capital letter.
lc	Use a lowercase letter.
p	Correct a punctuation error.
exact	Use a more exact word.
?	What does this mean?
∽	Transpose these letters.

Name _____

Editor's Checklist

Use this checklist to proofread and revise your writing. Make a check in the box when you have edited your writing for each item. Give this checklist to your teacher with your writing assignment.

Edit for:	Student Check ✔	Teacher Comments	Score
I. Development of Ideas/Content A. Is the purpose of my writing clear? B. Is my writing focused on the topic I'm writing about? C. Did I support my ideas with details, facts, and examples? D. Did I write appropriately for my audience?	☐ ☐ ☐ ☐		
II. Organization A. Is my writing clear and logical? B. Do I have a strong, interesting beginning that gets the reader's attention? C. Are my ideas tied together? Do I use transitions? D. Do I have a strong ending that ties things together?	☐ ☐ ☐ ☐		
III. Sentence Structure A. Are my sentences complete? Do they have a subject and a verb? B. Did I make sure I don't have any run-on sentences or fragments? C. Did I use different types of sentences—compound and complex?	☐ ☐ ☐		
IV. Grammar and Usage A. Is my writing in the right tense (for example, present or past)? B. Did I use subject pronouns and object pronouns correctly—*I/me, he/him, she/her, we/us, they/them?* C. Did I use the pronouns *she, her,* or *hers* for women and girls and *he, him,* or *his* for men and boys? D. Do my verbs agree with their subjects? Did I use singular verbs with singular subjects and plural verbs with plural subjects?	☐ ☐ ☐ ☐		

Name _____

Editor's Checklist (cont . . .)

Edit for:	Student Check ☑	Teacher Comments	Score

V. Word Choice
   A. Did I choose vivid and exact words? Did I use a thesaurus, glossary, or dictionary to help me choose better words?
   B. Did I eliminate extra words so that my writing is not wordy?
	☐
	
	☐		

VI. Writing Conventions
  Form
   A. Did I write my name, the date, and a title on the page?
   B. Did I indent the first line of each paragraph?
   C. Did I include a bibliography and correctly cite any references that I used?
   D. Did I create an attractive computer presentation, or did I use my best handwriting?
 	
  Spelling
   E. Did I check the spelling of all words I'm not sure about?
   F. If I wrote my paper on a computer, did I use spell check?
 	
  Capitalization
   G. Did I capitalize the names of proper nouns, such as people's names and the names of cities and countries?
   H. Did I start each sentence with a capital letter?
 	
  Punctuation
   I. Did I punctuate each sentence with the right mark (., ?, or !)?
   J. Did I put quotation marks around any direct speech?
   K. Did I use apostrophes correctly in contractions and possessives?
	☐
	☐
	☐
	
	☐
	
	☐
	☐
	
	☐
	☐
	
	☐
	☐
	☐		

VII. My Own Criteria
   A.
 	
   B.
 	
   C.
	☐
	
	☐
	
	☐		

Narrative Checklist

Use this checklist to evaluate your own writing and your classmates' writing.

_____ **Interesting title**

_____ **Name**

_____ **Date**

Introduction

1. _____ describes the setting

2. _____ introduces the characters

3. _____ introduces the problem or topic

Body

1. _____ describes an event

2. _____ gives details about the event

3. _____ uses sequence to relate events (throughout)

1. _____ describes an event

2. _____ gives details about the event

3. _____ uses strong verbs and vivid adjectives (throughout)

1. _____ brings problem to climax

2. _____ builds suspense for reader

3. _____ uses figurative language so the reader can "see," "taste," "hear," and "feel" the events (throughout)

Conclusion or Resolution

1. _____ restates problem

2. _____ shows how problem is resolved

3. _____ has a strong ending

_____ I used the Editor's Checklist to edit and revise this narrative.

Name _____

Persuasive Checklist

Use this checklist to evaluate your own writing and your classmates' writing.

_____ **Interesting title**

_____ **Name**

_____ **Date**

Introduction

1. _____ asks a question

2. _____ answers a question

3. _____ gives 3 supporting reasons for answer

Body

1. _____ begins with "First, . . ."

2. _____ restates reason # 1

3. _____ gives three supporting details/examples

1. _____ begins with "Next, . . ."

2. _____ restates reason # 2

3. _____ gives three supporting details/examples

1. _____ begins with "Finally, . . ."

2. _____ restates reason # 3

3. _____ gives three supporting details/examples

Conclusion

1. _____ begins with "In conclusion . . ."

2. _____ restates introduction answer

3. _____ restates 3 supporting reasons

_____ I used the Editor's Checklist to edit and revise this persuasive writing.

Name _____ Date _____

Oral Presentation Evaluation Sheet

Topic or Title _____

Presenter or Group _____

Did the presenter or group:	lowest		mid		highest
1. make use of eye contact and facial expressions?	1	2	3	4	5
2. have a good opening?	1	2	3	4	5
3. change the pitch and tone of voice?	1	2	3	4	5
4. use interesting and specific language?	1	2	3	4	5
5. use pauses or emphasis on key words?	1	2	3	4	5
6. support ideas with details and examples?	1	2	3	4	5
7. use gestures or action?	1	2	3	4	5
8. use visuals?	1	2	3	4	5
9. speak clearly?	1	2	3	4	5
10. have a good closing?	1	2	3	4	5

For a Reader's Theater or play

11. wear costumes or use props?	1	2	3	4	5
12. act so I believed the story?	1	2	3	4	5

Active Listening Checklist

Use this checklist to evaluate how well you listen and understand.

1. I liked _____ because _____
   _____

2. I want to know more about _____
   _____

3. I thought the opening was interesting.   ____ Yes ____ No

4. The speaker stayed on the topic.   ____ Yes ____ No

5. I did not understand _____
   _____

6. I needed the speaker to repeat or clarify _____
   _____

7. My own criteria: _____
   _____

8. My own criteria: _____
   _____

9. My own criteria: _____
   _____

Name _____ Date _____

Topic _____

Speaking Checklist

Use this checklist to evaluate your speaking.

1. Did I speak too slowly, too quickly, or just right? _____

2. Was the tone of my voice too high, too low, or just right? _____

3. Did I speak loudly enough for the audience to hear me?   ____ Yes ____ No

4. Did I produce the correct intonation patterns of sentences? ____ Yes ____ No

5. Did I have a good opening?   ____ Yes ____ No

6. Did I look at my audience?   ____ Yes ____ No

7. Did I speak with feeling?   ____ Yes ____ No

8. Did I support my ideas with facts and examples?   ____ Yes ____ No

9. Did I tell the audience how I feel about the topic?   ____ Yes ____ No

10. Did I use interesting, specific words?   ____ Yes ____ No

11. Did I use visuals to make the speech interesting?   ____ Yes ____ No

My Own Criteria

12. _____   ____ Yes ____ No

13. _____   ____ Yes ____ No

14. _____   ____ Yes ____ No

Viewing Checklist

Visuals help you understand texts and presentations better. Analyzing visuals for their usefulness will help you to learn how to create good visuals. Think about these points as you view and create visuals.

1. Do I understand the purpose of this visual?   ____ Yes ____ No

2. What is the purpose? _____
_____

3. Does this visual help me to understand better?   ____ Yes ____ No

4. How does it help me understand? _____
_____

5. Is the visual labeled clearly?   ____ Yes ____ No

6. Does the visual give me extra information?   ____ Yes ____ No

7. What did I learn from the visual? _____
_____

8. Would I create the same visual for this text/presentation?   ____ Yes ____ No

9. What would I do differently? _____
_____

10. My own viewing criteria: _____
_____

11. My own viewing criteria: _____
_____

Name ——————

Date ——————

Word Study and Spelling

Keep a list of new words that you learn. Use a dictionary, a glossary, or the Newbury House Dictionary CD-ROM to find definitions.

Word	Page	Sentence from Reading	Definition	Your Sentence

Name _____

Date _____

Word Study and Spelling Assessment Chart

1. Exchange your *Word Study and Spelling* pages with a partner.
2. Choose five words and ask your partner to spell them on a piece of paper.
3. Choose another five words and ask your partner to write a sentence using each.
4. Check your partner's work.
5. Record the number of words spelled correctly in the first row of your partner's chart.
6. Record the number of words used correctly in a sentence in the second row.
7. Record the words that were spelled or used incorrectly in the third row.

My Score	Unit 1	Unit 2	Unit 3	Unit 4	Unit 5	Unit 6
How many words did I spell correctly?	Correct: Incorrect:	Correct: Incorrect:	Correct: Incorrect:	Correct: Incorrect:	Correct: Incorrect:	Correct: Incorrect:
How many words did I use in a sentence correctly?	Correct: Incorrect:	Correct: Incorrect:	Correct: Incorrect:	Correct: Incorrect:	Correct: Incorrect:	Correct: Incorrect:
Which words do I need to study?						

Name _____

Independent Reading Record

Keep track of your reading here. Share this record with your classmates and talk about readings that you enjoyed.

Date	Title of Reading and Author	Reading Time	Pages Read	Comments
Sept. 2	The Pearl by John Steinbeck	20 minutes	pp. 60–85	Could relate to Kino's thoughts and feelings; great ending!

Name _____ Date _____

Student Self-Assessment

Part I: Circle the number that best describes you.

How I feel about my work in English:	Unhappy	1	2	3	4	Happy
My speaking and listening are:	Not Improving	1	2	3	4	Improving
My reading is:	Not Improving	1	2	3	4	Improving
My writing is:	Not Improving	1	2	3	4	Improving
My work is:	Too Hard	1	2	3	4	Too Easy
My work is:	Not Interesting	1	2	3	4	Very Interesting

Part II: Complete these sentences.

1. The best thing that I did/learned lately is _____

_____

2. I would like to learn _____

_____

3. I am best at _____

_____

4. I need some help with _____

_____

5. My learning and practicing plans are to _____

_____

Name _____ Date _____

Activity and Project Reflection

Think about the activities and projects that you have done in class. Then answer these questions.

1. The most interesting activity or project that we did was _____

_____

2. I think this activity or project was interesting because _____

_____

_____

_____

_____

3. In this activity or project, I learned _____

_____

_____

_____

_____

4. Did anyone else work with you or help you with your learning? How did he or

she help you? _____

_____

_____

_____

Test-Taking Tips

Use these tips to help you improve your performance on tests.

BEFORE THE TEST

1. Complete all of your assignments on time.

2. Take notes in class as you go over your assignments.

3. Save and review your class notes, assignments, and quizzes.

4. Ask your teacher what topics will be covered on the test.

5. Ask your teacher what kind of test you will take. For example, will the questions be true/false, multiple choice, or essay?

6. Be organized. Make a study guide. Making note cards or rewriting information will help you review.

7. Study, and then get a good night's sleep before the test.

8. Eat a good, healthy breakfast on the day of the test.

9. Bring everything that you need to the test (pencils, erasers, pens, and so on).

DURING THE TEST

1. Pay close attention to the teacher's instructions. Ask questions if you do not understand.

2. Read the instructions on the test carefully.

3. Look at the test before you begin to see how long it is.

4. Don't spend too much time on any one section or question. Skip questions that you don't know. Return to them if you have time at the end.

5. Watch the time to make sure you finish the whole test.

6. Save time to look over the test before you turn it in. Don't worry if other students finish before you. Use all the time that you have.

AFTER THE TEST

1. When your test is returned to you, look at it carefully.

2. Look up the answers to any questions you left blank or got wrong.

3. Ask your teacher about any questions that you still don't understand. The same question might appear again on another test.

⇨

TYPES OF TEST QUESTIONS

TRUE/FALSE STATEMENTS

Decide if the following statement is *true* or *false*.

> _False_   **1.** All trees lose their leaves in the winter.

1. Read the statements carefully.
2. Look for anything in the statement that is not true. If any detail is false, then the whole statement is false.
3. Watch out for absolute words like *always, all, never, no, best,* and *worst*. These may be clues that the statement is false.

MULTIPLE-CHOICE QUESTIONS

Choose the correct answer from the list of choices.

> **1.** Which type of tree loses its leaves in the fall?
>   **a.** coniferous tree   **b.** pine tree   **(c.)** deciduous tree   **d.** fir tree

1. Read the question carefully before you look at the answer choices.
2. Answer the question before you look at the choices. Then see if your answer is listed.
3. Read all of the answers before you choose one.
4. If you are not sure which answer is correct, cross out the ones that you know are wrong. Choose one of the answers that is left.

ESSAY QUESTIONS

Write one or more paragraphs to answer the question.

> **1.** Describe three things that happen to deciduous trees in the fall.

1. Know what you are being asked to do (for example, *describe, discuss, compare, explain,* and so on).
2. Plan your essay before you begin to write. Making a basic outline first will help you stay focused.
3. Include a *thesis statement, supporting evidence,* and a *conclusion.*
4. Show how much you know, but stay focused. Include only information that is relevant to your topic or thesis.
5. Write neatly. Your teacher must be able to read your answer.

Lesson Plan Checklist

for *The Sheltered Instruction Observation Protocol*

I. PREPARATION

_____ Write content objectives clearly for students.

_____ Write language objectives clearly for students.

_____ Choose content concepts appropriate for age and educational background level of students.

_____ Identify supplementary materials to use (graphs, models, visuals).

_____ Adapt content (e.g., text, assignment) to all levels of student proficiency.

_____ Plan meaningful activities that integrate lesson concepts (e.g., surveys, letter writing, simulations, constructing models) with language practice opportunities for reading, writing, listening, and/or speaking.

II. INSTRUCTION

Building Background

_____ Explicitly link concepts to students' backgrounds and experiences.

_____ Explicitly link past learning and new concepts.

_____ Emphasize key vocabulary (e.g., introduce, write, repeat, and highlight for students to see).

Comprehensible Input

_____ Use speech appropriate for students' proficiency level (e.g., slower rate, enunciation, and simple sentence structure for beginners).

_____ Explain academic tasks clearly.

_____ Use a variety of techniques to make content concepts clear (e.g., modeling, visuals, hands-on activities, demonstrations, gestures, body language).

Strategies

_____ Provide ample opportunities for students to use strategies (e.g., problem solving, predicting, organizing, summarizing, categorizing, evaluating, self-monitoring).

_____ Use scaffolding techniques consistently (providing the right amount of support to move students from one level of understanding to a higher level) throughout the lesson.

_____ Use a variety of question types throughout the lesson, including those that promote higher-order thinking skills throughout the lesson (e.g., literal, analytical, and interpretive questions).

Short, D., and Ecchevaria, J. (1999). *The Sheltered Instruction Observation Protocol: A Tool for Teacher-Researcher Collaboration and Professional Development.* Center for Research on Education, Diversity & Excellence, University of California, Santa Cruz.

Lesson Plan Checklist (cont . . .)

for *The Sheltered Instruction Observation Protocol*

Interaction

_____ Provide frequent opportunities for interaction and discussion between teacher/student and among students about lessons and concepts, and encourage elaborated responses.

_____ Use group configurations that support language and content objectives of the lesson.

_____ Consistently provide sufficient wait time for student responses.

_____ Give ample opportunities for students to clarify key concepts in L1 as needed with aide, peer, or L1 text.

Practice/Application

_____ Provide hands-on materials and/or manipulatives for students to practice using new content knowledge.

_____ Provide activities for students to apply content and language knowledge in the classroom.

_____ Use activities that integrate all language skills (reading, writing, listening, and speaking).

Lesson Delivery

_____ Support content objectives clearly.

_____ Support language objectives clearly.

_____ Engage students approximately 90–100% of the period (with most students taking part in and working on task throughout the lesson).

_____ Pace the lesson appropriately to the students' ability level.

Review/Assessment

_____ Give a comprehensive review of key vocabulary.

_____ Give a comprehensive review of key content concepts.

_____ Provide feedback to students regularly on their output (e.g., language, content, work).

_____ Conduct assessments of student comprehension and learning throughout lesson on all lesson objectives (e.g., spot checking, group response) throughout the lesson.

Short, D., and Ecchevaria, J. (1999). *The Sheltered Instruction Observation Protocol: A Tool for Teacher-Researcher Collaboration and Professional Development.* Center for Research on Education, Diversity & Excellence, University of California, Santa Cruz.

Rubric for Oral Reading Fluency

adapted from the National Assessment of Educational Progress (NAEP)
Scale for Assessing Oral Reading Fluency

Point Scale	Description of Oral Reading Fluency
4	Reads primarily in large, meaningful phrase groups. Although some regressions, repetitions, and deviations from text may be present, these do not appear to detract from the overall structure of the story. Preservation of the author's syntax is consistent. Some or most of the story is read with expressive interpretation.
3	Reads primarily in three- or four-word phrase groups. Some smaller groupings may be present. However, the majority of phrasing seems appropriate and preserves the syntax of the author. Little or no expressive interpretation is present.
2	Reads primarily in two-word phrases with some three- or four-word groupings. Some word-by-word reading may be present. Word groupings may seem awkward and unrelated to the larger context of the sentence or passage.
1	Reads primarily word by word. Occasional two-word or three-word phrases may occur, but these are infrequent and/or they do not preserve meaningful syntax.

Rubric for Oral Presentations

	3 points	2 points	1 point
Presentation	• Student uses appropriate eye contact and facial expressions. • Student uses gestures consistently. • Student seems at ease and engages the audience.	• Student uses some eye contact and facial expressions. • Student makes some use of gestures. • Student begins to overcome timidity and engages the audience.	• Student uses no eye contact. • Student uses no gestures. • Student is remote and isolated from the audience.
Speaking Mechanics	• Student uses exciting pitch and tone of voice. • Student is clear and easily understood. • Student pauses and emphasizes key words.	• Student sometimes varies pitch and tone. • Student is sometimes difficult to hear. • Student uses some pauses and emphasis for key words.	• Student uses no change in pitch or tone. • Student is difficult to hear. • Student uses no pauses or emphasis for key words.
Content	• Opening and closing are good. • Grammar and word choice are easy to understand. • Central idea is supported with details and examples. • The speaker's individuality and perspective are clear.	• Opening and closing are perfunctory. • Grammar and word choice are usually appropriate. • Central idea is not fully developed. • There is some sense of the speaker's individual perspective.	• There is no opening or closing. • Grammar and word choice make the presentation hard to understand. • The central idea is not clear. • There is no sense of the speaker's individual perspective.
Visuals/ Props/ Costumes	• Visuals and props enhance and clarify presentation. • Costumes are appropriate for presentation (Reader's Theater).	• Visuals and props provide limited clarification and enhancement of presentation. • Costumes are somewhat appropriate for presentation (Reader's Theater).	• There are no visuals. • There are no props. • There are no costumes (Reader's Theater).

Name _____   Teacher _____

Grade _____   Semester/Year _____

RUBRIC		
	1. Limited progress	Little or no progress toward mastery of standard.
	2. Partial progress	Some progress toward mastery of standard.
	3. Average progress	Masters the standard for his/her level.
	4. Advanced progress	Exceeds the standard for his/her level.

LISTENING AND SPEAKING STANDARDS ASSESSMENT CHECKLIST	Marking Period and Scores			
	1	2	3	4
Listen actively and purposefully				
1. Determine purpose of listening, such as to gain information, to problem solve, to enjoy				
2. Eliminate barriers to effective listening				
3. Understand major ideas while listening				
4. Understand supporting evidence while listening				
5. Listen to take notes				
6. Listen to organize				
7. Listen to summarize				
8. Distinguish and produce sounds				
9. Distinguish and produce intonation patterns				
Total Points	/36	/36	/36	/36
Listen critically to analyze and evaluate a speaker's message				
10. Interpret verbal messages				
11. Interpret nonverbal messages				
12. Interpret purposes				
13. Interpret perspectives				
14. Identify and analyze speaker's persuasive techniques and credibility				
15. Distinguish the speaker's opinion from verifiable fact				
16. Self-monitor understanding of spoken message				
17. Seek clarification as needed				
18. Compare own perception of a message with others' perception				
19. Evaluate spoken message for content				
20. Evaluate spoken message for credibility				
21. Evaluate spoken message for delivery				
Total Points	/48	/48	/48	/48
Listen to enjoy and appreciate spoken language				
22. Listen to fluent readings of classic and contemporary works				
23. Analyze oral interpretations of literature for effects on the listener				
24. Analyze aesthetic language for its effects				
Total Points	/12	/12	/12	/12

⇨

LISTENING AND SPEAKING STANDARDS ASSESSMENT CHECKLIST (cont…)	Marking Period and Scores			
	1	2	3	4
Listen and speak to gain knowledge of culture				
25. Connect own information with the experiences of others				
26. Connect own insights with the experiences of others				
27. Connect own ideas with the experiences of others				
28. Compare oral traditions across regions				
29. Compare oral traditions across cultures				
30. Identify how language use, such as labels and sayings, reflects regions				
31. Identify how language use, such as labels and sayings, reflects cultures				
Total Points	/28	/28	/28	/28
Speak clearly and appropriately to different audiences on different occasions				
32. Adapt word choice to audience, purpose, and occasion				
33. Adapt diction to audience, purpose, and occasion				
34. Adapt usage to audience, purpose, and occasion				
35. Demonstrate communication skills—interviewing, reporting, requesting, and providing information				
36. Present dramatic interpretations of experiences				
37. Present dramatic interpretations of stories				
38. Present dramatic interpretations of poems or plays				
39. Generate criteria to evaluate own presentations				
40. Generate criteria to evaluate others' presentations				
41. Use effective rate for the audience and setting				
42. Use effective volume for the audience and setting				
43. Use effective pitch for the audience and setting				
44. Use effective tone for the audience and setting				
45. Clarify spoken ideas with evidence				
46. Clarify spoken ideas with elaboration				
47. Clarify spoken ideas with examples				
48. Support spoken ideas with evidence				
49. Support spoken ideas with elaboration				
50. Support spoken ideas with examples				
51. Employ content area vocabulary in context				
Total Points	/80	/80	/80	/80

Name _____   Teacher _____

Grade _____   Semester/Year _____

RUBRIC	**1.** Limited progress	Little or no progress toward mastery of standard.
	2. Partial progress	Some progress toward mastery of standard.
	3. Average progress	Masters the standard for his/her level.
	4. Advanced progress	Exceeds the standard for his/her level.

READING STANDARDS ASSESSMENT CHECKLIST	Marking Period and Scores			
	1	2	3	4
Use a variety of word recognition and analysis strategies				
1. Apply knowledge of letter-sound correspondences to words				
2. Apply knowledge of language structure to words				
3. Apply knowledge of context to words				
4. Identify prefixes and suffixes				
5. Identify Greek and Latin root words				
6. Locate word meanings, pronunciations, and derivations in dictionaries, glossaries, and other sources				
Total Points	/24	/24	/24	/24
Read with fluency and understanding in texts at appropriate difficulty levels				
7. Read regularly in independent-level and instructional-level materials				
8. Read aloud to reflect understanding of text and engage listeners				
9. Read silently with increasing ease for longer periods				
10. Adjust reading rate for purpose				
Total Points	/16	/16	/16	/16
Read widely for different purposes in varied sources				
11. Read classic and contemporary texts				
12. Read in varied sources, such as plays, novels, newspapers, textbooks, and electronic texts				
13. Read for varied purposes, such as for information, entertainment, and appreciation of craft				
14. Read to take action, such as to complete forms, respond, and make a recommendation				
Total Points	/16	/16	/16	/16
Acquire an extensive vocabulary through reading and systematic word study				
15. Develop vocabulary by listening to selections read aloud				
16. Draw on experiences to interpret words in context, such as figurative language, multiple-meaning words, and analogies				
17. Use multiple reference aids to clarify meaning and usage, such as a thesaurus, a synonym finder, a dictionary, and software				
18. Determine meanings of derivatives by knowledge of root words and affixes				
19. Study word meanings systematically				
20. Distinguish denotative and connotative meanings				
21. Use word origins to understand historical influences on word meanings				
Total Points	/28	/28	/28	/28
Use a variety of strategies to comprehend a wide range of texts of increasing levels of difficulty				
22. Use own knowledge and experience to comprehend texts				
23. Establish and adjust purposes for reading				
24. Monitor own comprehension				
25. Make modifications when understanding breaks down—rereading portions aloud, using reference aids, searching for clues, and asking questions				
26. Describe mental images that texts evoke				

⇨

READING STANDARDS ASSESSMENT CHECKLIST (cont…)	Marking Period and Scores			
	1	2	3	4
27. Use text structure and progression of ideas to locate and recall information				
28. Determine main ideas and supporting details				
29. Paraphrase and summarize text to recall, inform, or organize ideas				
30. Draw inferences, such as conclusions or generalizations				
31. Support inferences with text evidence and experience				
32. Find similarities and differences across texts				
33. Distinguish fact and opinion in various texts				
34. Answer different types and levels of questions—open-ended, literal, interpretive, multiple choice, true/false, and short answer				
35. Represent text information in different ways—outlines, timelines, and graphic organizers				
36. Use strategies to learn important ideas, such as preview, question, reread, and record				
37. Use strategies to recall important ideas, such as preview, question, reread, and record				
Total Points	/64	/64	/64	/64
Express and support responses to various types of texts				
38. Offer observations, make connections, react, speculate, interpret, and raise questions in response to texts				
39. Interpret text ideas through journal writing, discussion, enactment, and media				
40. Support responses by referring to relevant aspects of text and own experiences				
41. Connect, compare, and contrast ideas, themes, and issues across texts				
Total Points	/16	/16	/16	/16
Analyze the characteristics of various types of text (genres)				
42. Identify purposes of different types of text—to inform, entertain, influence, or express				
43. Recognize distinguishing features of genres, including biography, historical fiction, informational text, and poetry				
44. Compare communication in different forms				
45. Understand and identify literary terms				
46. Understand literary forms by recognizing types of text				
47. Understand literary forms by distinguishing among types of text				
48. Analyze characters for traits, motivation, conflicts, points of view, relationships, and changes				
49. Recognize and analyze story plot, setting, and problem resolution				
50. Describe how the author's point of view or perspective affects the text				
51. Analyze ways authors organize and present ideas				
52. Recognize and interpret literary devices—flashback, foreshadowing, and symbolism				
53. Recognize how style, tone, and mood contribute to the effect of a text				
Total Points	/48	/48	/48	/48
Inquire and conduct research using a variety of sources				
54. Form and revise questions for investigations				
55. Use text organizers to locate information—headings, graphics, and tables of contents				
56. Use multiple sources to locate research information—electronic texts, print, and experts				
57. Interpret and use graphic sources of information (maps, charts, timelines, and tables) to address research questions				
58. Summarize and organize information from multiple sources in notes, outlines, or charts				
59. Produce research projects and reports in effective formats for various audiences				
60. Draw conclusions from information gathered from multiple sources				
61. Use compiled information and knowledge to raise additional questions				
62. Present organized statements, reports, and speeches using visuals				
Total Points	/36	/36	/36	/36
Read to increase knowledge of own culture, the culture of others, and the common elements of cultures				
63. Compare text events with own experiences and other readers' experiences				
64. Determine distinctive and common characteristics of cultures				
65. Articulate and discuss themes and connections that cross cultures				
Total Points	/12	/12	/12	/12

RUBRIC		
	1. Limited progress	Little or no progress toward mastery of standard.
	2. Partial progress	Some progress toward mastery of standard.
	3. Average progress	Masters the standard for his/her level.
	4. Advanced progress	Exceeds the standard for his/her level.

WRITING STANDARDS ASSESSMENT CHECKLIST	Marking Period and Scores			
	1	2	3	4
Write for a variety of purposes and audiences and in a variety of forms				
1. Write to express				
2. Write to discover				
3. Write to record				
4. Write to develop				
5. Write to reflect on ideas				
6. Write to problem solve				
7. Write to influence—persuade, request, and argue				
8. Write to inform—explain, narrate, describe, and report				
9. Write to entertain—humorous poems or short stories				
10. Select and use voice and style appropriate to audience				
11. Select and use voice and style appropriate to purpose				
12. Choose appropriate form for purpose—journal, letter, editorial, review, poem, memoir, narrative, and instructional text				
13. Use literary devices effectively—suspense, dialogue, and figurative language				
14. Produce cohesive and coherent texts by organizing ideas				
15. Produce cohesive and coherent texts by using effective transitions				
16. Produce cohesive and coherent texts by choosing precise wording				
Total Points	/64	/64	/64	/64
Compose original texts applying the conventions of written language, such as capitalization, punctuation, penmanship, and spelling, to communicate clearly				
17. Write legibly, using cursive or manuscript as appropriate				
18. Capitalize correctly to clarify and enhance meaning				
19. Punctuate correctly to clarify and enhance meaning				
20. Spell: open and closed syllables, consonant before -le, syllable boundary patterns				
21. Write with accurate spelling of roots, inflections, suffixes, and prefixes				
22. Spell derivatives correctly by applying the spelling of bases				
23. Spell derivatives correctly by applying the spelling of affixes				
24. Spell frequently misspelled words, such as *their, they're, there*				
25. Use resources to find correct spellings				
26. Spell accurately in final drafts				
27. Understand the influence of languages and cultures on spelling				
Total Points	/44	/44	/44	/44
Apply standard grammar and usage to communicate clearly and effectively in writing				
28. Use regular and irregular plurals correctly				
29. Write varying sentence types—compound and complex				
30. Write correctly punctuated independent and dependent clauses				
31. Use conjunctions to connect ideas				
32. Use subject-verb agreement				
33. Use pronoun referents				
34. Use parts of speech				
35. Use adjectives—regular, comparative, and superlative				

VISIONS TEACHER RESOURCE

WRITING STANDARDS ASSESSMENT CHECKLIST (cont...)	Marking Period and Scores			
	1	**2**	**3**	**4**
36. Use adverbs				
37. Use prepositional phrases				
38. Use verb tenses appropriately and consistently—present, past, future, perfect, progressive				
39. Use apostrophes in contractions and possessives				
40. Use pronoun case				
Total Points	/52	/52	/52	/52

Select and use writing processes for self-initiated and assigned writing

41. Generate ideas and plans for prewriting—brainstorming, graphic organizers, notes, and logs				
42. Develop drafts by categorizing ideas				
43. Develop drafts by organizing ideas into paragraphs				
44. Develop drafts by blending paragraphs within larger units of text				
45. Revise drafts by adding and elaborating text				
46. Revise drafts by deleting text				
47. Revise drafts by combining text				
48. Revise drafts by rearranging text				
49. Revise drafts for coherence				
50. Revise drafts for progression				
51. Revise drafts for logical support of ideas				
52. Edit drafts for specific purposes— word choice, sentence structure, and standard usage				
53. Use technology to create, revise, edit, and publish texts				
54. Refine pieces to publish for general and specific audiences				
55. Proofread own writing and others' writing				
56. Select and use reference materials and resources for writing				
57. Select and use reference materials and resources for revising and editing final drafts				
Total Points	/68	/68	/68	/68

Evaluate own writing and the writing of others

58. Apply criteria to evaluate writing				
59. Respond constructively to others' writing				
60. Evaluate own writing to achieve purposes				
61. Analyze published examples				
62. Review written works to determine strengths and weaknesses				
63. Review written works to set goals as a writer				
Total Points	/24	/24	/24	/24

Use writing as a tool for learning and research

64. Frame questions to direct research				
65. Organize prior knowledge about a topic in a variety of ways				
66. Take notes from relevant and authoritative sources				
67. Summarize ideas gained from multiple sources				
68. Organize ideas gained from multiple sources				
69. Use technology to present information				
70. Evaluate own research				
71. Frame new questions for further investigation				
72. Document research sources				
Total Points	/36	/36	/36	/36

Interact with writers inside and outside the classroom in ways that reflect the practical use of writing

73. Collaborate with others to compose letters, news, records, and forms				
74. Collaborate with others to organize letters, news, records, and forms				
75. Collaborate with others to revise letters, news, records, and forms				
76. Use E-mail or conventional mail				
77. Identify challenges that published authors face				
78. Identify writing strategies that published authors use				
Total Points	/24	/24	/24	/24

Name _____   Teacher _____

Grade _____   Semester/Year _____

RUBRIC	**1.** Limited progress	Little or no progress toward mastery of standard.
	2. Partial progress	Some progress toward mastery of standard.
	3. Average progress	Masters the standard for his/her level.
	4. Advanced progress	Exceeds the standard for his/her level.

VIEWING AND REPRESENTING STANDARDS ASSESSMENT CHECKLIST	Marking Period and Scores			
	1	2	3	4
Understand and interpret visual images, messages, and meanings				
1. Describe how text meanings are communicated through illustrator's style				
2. Describe how text meanings are communicated through illustrator's elements				
3. Describe how text meanings are communicated through illustrator's media				
4. Interpret events gathered from maps, charts, graphics, video, or technology				
5. Interpret ideas gathered from maps, charts, graphics, video, or technology				
6. Use media to compare ideas				
7. Use media to compare points of view				
Total Points	/28	/28	/28	/28
Analyze and critique the significance of visual images, messages, and meanings				
8. Interpret how visual image makers, such as illustrators, documentary filmmakers, and political cartoonists, represent meaning				
9. Evaluate how visual image makers, such as illustrators, documentary filmmakers, and political cartoonists, represent meaning				
10. Compare print media with written story				
11. Contrast print media with written story				
12. Compare visual media with written story				
13. Contrast visual media with written story				
14. Compare electronic media with written story				
15. Contrast electronic media with written story				
16. Evaluate the purposes of various media, such as film, print, and technology presentations				
17. Evaluate the effects of various media, such as film, print, and technology presentations				
18. Evaluate how media forms influence				
19. Evaluate how media forms inform				
Total Points	/48	/48	/48	/48
Produce visual images, messages, and meanings that communicate with others				
20. Select, organize, or produce visuals to complement meaning				
21. Select, organize, or produce visuals to extend meaning				
22. Use technology or media to produce communications, such as a class newspaper, multimedia report, or video report				
23. Assess how language contributes to the message				
24. Assess how the medium contributes to the message				
25. Assess how presentation contributes to the message				
Total Points	/24	/24	/24	/2